EVOLUTION
EXPOSED

EVOLUTION EXPOSED

PAUL G. HUMBER
FOREWORD BY DUANE T. GISH

A Division of WINEPRESS PUBLISHING

ISBN 1-4141-0612-2
Library of Congress Catalog Card Number: 2005910341

TABLE OF CONTENTS

Introduction   xix
The *Philadelphia Inquirer* reported a debate in May of
2005 involving a biology professor and the author.
Whereas this debate had little effect in changing the
minds of either participant, a second exchange, also
in 2005, may have helped the evolutionary professor
involved to gain new perspectives.

Chapter 1: Interaction with Evolutionists   29
The author is pictured with Dr. Brian Richmond of
George Washington University's Anthropology Department. The seminal article, *The Ascent of Racism*, is updated in this chapter.

**Chapter 2: Was My Article, Translated and Published
in Various Languages, in Error?**   39
One evolutionist took the author to task. He claimed that
Hitler hardly used the word, "evolution," in his book, but
this was misleading. After shown to be in error, however,
the evolutionist eventually reverted to calling the author
a moron and a liar. There is hope, however.

Chapter 3: Scientific Evidence for Creation   49

Twenty-five reasons to choose creation over evolution are provided. Homeschoolers especially may find this summary helpful in countering textbooks which display evolutionary bias.

Chapter 4: Recreational Creation   69

The author shares personal experiences which point to the graciousness of Creator Christ.

Chapter 5: Up Close and Personal with Creator Christ   75

Continuing with the uplifting theme, the author relates experiences he personally had with Creator Christ. One of these is reinforced by electronic images of his son's brain before and after surgery. Seen together, they provide tangible evidence that one can commune with and realistically hope for answers from the Creator.

Chapter 6: Do Creationists Believe the Earth Is Flat?   81

Ridicule of creationists as flat-earthers is vacuous. Christopher Columbus was/is a devout creationist!

Chapter 7: An Open Door for Creation to Be Taught in Public Schools   89

There are opportunities to teach creation science consistent with biblical truth to America's public school children. Many people are unaware of this and can act upon the information provided.

Chapter 8: My Interaction with Oxford's Richard Dawkins   103

This chapter concerns many e-mail exchanges the author had with Dr. Richard Dawkins of Oxford University, perhaps the world's best known spokesman for evolution.

Remarkable facts followed, including two apologies from Dr. Dawkins.

Chapter 9: Something Many People Do Not Realize About Joseph Stalin   119
In chapter one, evolutionism gave supposed legitimacy to Hitler's actions. Many people do not realize, however, that Joseph Stalin, perhaps an even greater blight upon human history, explicitly rejected the Bible in favor of Darwin. Evolution's hellish roots are exposed in this chapter.

Chapter 10: A Beautiful American Biologist   127
In connection with the author's work (facilitating Christian released time among Philadelphia's public school children—see chapter seven), he was asked to be the guest speaker for a commencement and talked about the Creation Scientist, George Washington Carver.

Chapter 11: Something Presently Exists in America That Is Far Worse Even Than Slavery!   133
This chapter, a sequel to the previous, actually points to a current crisis in America. Evolutionary thinking not only fostered racial slavery in the past, it promotes the slaughter of unborn children in America today by the millions. As documented, a disproportionate number of minority children are slaughtered in American aborturaries. This is a form of racism—of the worst kind.

Chapter 12: Subtle Sanger   139
Continuing with the deadly theme of the previous chapter, this new one exposes Margaret Sanger, the founder of Planned Parenthood, as a practicing evolutionist. It also reveals that Carl Sagan's "biological" justification for abortion, based on evolutionary nonsense, is absurd.

Chapter 13: Darwin Got "His" Key Thought from a Creationist!　147

Dr. Loren Eiseley, an evolutionary professor at the University of Pennsylvania while the author studied there, exposed Darwin as a probable plagiarizer—as one who "borrowed" ideas from a creation scientist without giving proper credit.

Chapter 14: "Doesn't Geology Prove Evolution?"　153

The author had personal correspondence (extending over four months) with the editor of *The American Atheist*. The exchanges were cordial and dealt extensively with one of the atheist's main "proofs" in support of evolution, the so-called varves of the Green River Formation. This main proof is weak.

Chapter 15: In General, the Religion of Islam Affirms Creation　169

This chapter considers creationary teaching in the Koran. Many people today are curious about what Muslims believe, and it is somewhat encouraging to know that Muslims, at least as far as the Koran is concerned, are more on the side of creation than evolution.

Chapter 16: If Creation Is True, Why Does Evil Exist?　177

The author shares a letter to a colleague of his at the Haverford School. How can ugly things in the world be harmonized with faith in a loving God? This chapter deals with God's cosmic purpose in the universe.

Chapter 17: Creation and Death　189

Creation has to do with beginnings, but what about the ugly specter of death (the endings)? In a personal and tangible way, this chapter shows that even death itself must give way to the Creator and Recreator. Death's sorrow on September 3, 1939, for example, is swallowed up even now in recreationary hope. The last enemy to be destroyed is death.

Chapter 18: A Verbal Message on a Pebble-like Coin 195
There is good evidence that the coin pictured in this chapter was near the feet of Jesus when He entered Jerusalem on the first Palm Sunday. Moreover, the very brief message on this pebble-like coin supports the words spoken by Jesus on that eventful day. Its small "peep" has wide ramifications throughout the universe.

Chapter 19: Are Dinosaurs Really Millions of Years Old? 199
Many orthodox Christians hold to an "old" universe, but is doing so scientifically necessary? If the universe is billions of years old, then how can this be reconciled with biblical chronology? Scientific evidence is given that the world/universe is not anywhere near as old as evolutionists proclaim.

Chapter 20: Mathematical Creation 215
Having taught mathematics to high school and college students for decades, the author came to appreciate more and more the vast improbability of evolution. Mathematics, the language of nature, is also the language of science.

Chapter 21: Evolutionary Hypocrisy 225
This concerns a professor at Penn (now at Princeton) who promoted the display and selling of misleading cranial models while at the same time disallowing the sale of a videotaped debate allegedly because he did not believe "fossil" finds of his creationary opponent in the

debate were legitimate. The author served as debate moderator.

Chapter 22: *Inherit the Wind*—Evolutionary Propaganda 231

An interesting aspect of this chapter is a letter written to the author from famed actor Kirk Douglas, the one who played the part of the character representing William Jennings Bryan. Mr. Douglas admitted in his personal letter that aspects of his portrayal were deliberately enacted to misrepresent Bryan.

Chapter 23: Humanism's Faith in Evolution 239

Documentation is offered that exposes atheistic humanism (having evolution as a main tenet) as religion foisted on American public school children. This stems from the author's experience as a teacher at Abington High School. He had personal knowledge of and interaction with his friend, Dr. Allan Glatthorn, who then served as principal.

Conclusion: "Out of Focus" Evolution—Getting Closer! 243

Evolutionist Dr. Loren Eiseley admitted to a pulling away from evolutionary thinking. Coming from such an evolutionary authority, this is revealing. The author concludes with a prayer he gave at the 2001 Haverford School commencement in the name of the Creator.

Appendix 1: Autobiography   247
Appendix 2: Hitler's Evolutionary Words in Context   251
Endnotes   255

FOREWORD

Paul Humber's *Evolution Exposed*, is a book that should be possessed by everyone who is interested in the scientific and biblical evidence for creation. It contains information that is not found in most, if any, other books defending the truth of God's creation. He documents extensively the wide acceptance of racism by evolutionists such as Charles Darwin, Ernst Haekel, Henry Fairfield Osborn, and others, and how this undergirded the philosophy of Adolph Hitler. He cites the testimony of evolutionist Loren Eiseley that "the leading tenets of Darwin's work–the struggle for existence, variation, natural selection, and sexual selection–are all fully expressed in a paper written by creationist Edward Blyth in 1835" (Loren Eiseley, *Darwin and the Mysterious Mr. X*). Humber includes quotes from several of Blyth's essays published in 1835, 1836, and 1837 that reveal his grasp of natural science and his devotion to God as Creator, "…which by the unity of design pervading which all is demonstrable to be the workmanship of one omnipotent and all-foreseeing providence…"

Richard Dawkins is currently a professor at Oxford University, an outspoken atheist, and evolutionary biologist who has authored a number of books intended to support Darwinian evolution. Chapter eight of *Evolution Exposed* is a description of an extensive exchange of correspondence between Humber and Dawkins in 2003 concerning the debate that took place between Dawkins, John Maynard Smith, and creationists A. L. Wilder-Smith and Edgar Andrews at the Oxford Union, February 14, 1986. In the exchange Dawkins initially claimed that he and Maynard Smith won the debate 198 to 15, but finally acknowledged that the correct figure was most likely 198 to 115. The fact that the creationists received 115 votes of 313 cast from those at Oxford University, who would be highly partisan due to steady indoctrination by Dawkins and others at Oxford, would have to be considered a considerable moral victory by Wilder-Smith and Andrews, whom Dawkins attempted to ridicule in his correspondence. Wilder-Smith was a brilliant scientist with three earned PhD's from European universities and Andrews was a scientist whose outstanding credentials needed no support. This exchange between Humber and Dawkins alone would be worth the price of the book.

Many other chapters in *Evolution Exposed*, such as those on atheism and evolution, the Green River Shales, Islam and Creation, the age of creation, mathematical creation, and humanism's faith in evolution, to name a few, will hold the reader's attention as Humber provides new insights while exploring many aspects of the creation/evolution debate, all written in an easily readable fashion. Throughout his book Humber expresses adoration and honor to the God of creation.

Duane T. Gish, PhD
Senior Vice President Emeritus
Institute for Creation Research

ACKNOWLEDGMENTS

I wish to thank Cecil Allen for the photographs of dinosaur fossils on the front and back covers. They were taken in 2005 at the Museum of the Rockies in Bozeman, Montana. (Incidentally, that museum, like Dr. Stringer referred to below, probably does not support many of the views offered in the following pages.) I would like, also, to thank both Doug Sharp for the background photograph on the front cover[1] and Chris Fox[2] for the other picture on the back cover. Skilton House Ministries, Inc., of which I serve as Executive Director, is assuming a significant portion of the expenses associated with the publication of this book. Additionally, I thank and/or acknowledge the following who have helped me directly or indirectly to improve this book to its present level: Harry Akers, Kevin Anderson, Millie Berghaus, David Bradbury, Kay Brigham, Ruth Brittain, Linda Brown, Donald Brownlow, Joseph Cox, Jack Cuozzo, Richard Dawkins, Kirk Douglas, Loren Eiseley, Michael Erkel, Ed Garrett, Robert Gentet, Duane Gish, Dean Gray, Edward Hallowell, David Harris, Charles Humber, Evelyn Humber, Paul Humber (Jr.), Peter Humber, Prudence Humber, Russell Humphreys, Priscilla Hurlbut, Ian Juby, Lane Lester, Herbert Oliver, Ron Pass, Todd Pearson, Anna Rolen, Cynthia Ruble, Dave Sack, Helen Setterfield, Curt Sewell, John Skilton, Mark Stewart, MaryAnn Stuart, Laurence Tisdall, Sharon Traver, Fred Weir, Glen Wolfrom, Alfred Youssef, and Frank Zindler. Preeminently, I acknowledge the moment by moment patience and presence of the Lord Jesus Christ Himself, Who made me and all of the above. Thank You, Jehovah Jesus, Creator Christ, Supreme Savior! May the beauty You have displayed in minute detail and on grand scale be credited in increasing numbers by many to You and not to the nonentities of mother nature and blind evolution.

"Good Luck" from a Fellow of the Royal Society (FRS)

Various Fellows of the Royal Society are referred to in this book. Creationist Isaac Newton and Evolutionist Charles Darwin may be among the more famous. (To give you an idea of how old this Fellowship is, Newton became a Fellow in 1672!) Evolutionist Richard Dawkins became a Fellow in 2001, and chapter eight of this book deals extensively with e-mail interactions with him.

On August 29, 2005, I sent a message to Professor Christopher Stringer, Head of Human Origins, Department of Paleontology, the Natural History Museum, London, England, who became a Fellow of the Royal Society in 2004. As I had had previous contact with Dr. Stringer concerning a creation-evolution debate I had moderated, I asked if he would have an interest in looking over a draft of my book. I thought he might be curious about what an American creationist might be writing. In fact, I even invited him to offer a few comments, if he found any "worthwhile aspects" in the book.

He graciously responded on September 2, 2005, thanking me for the offer; nevertheless, he declined, referring among other things to a public debate he had had with Dr. Duane Gish, the author of this book's Foreword. Though Dr. Stringer undoubtedly sees things differently than either Dr. Gish or I, he nevertheless ended his message to me with, "But good luck with the book. Best, Chris." (Reference is made to my previous interactions with Dr. Stringer in chapter twenty-one.)

STATEMENT OF PURPOSE

The purpose of this book is to expose many of the weaknesses in evolutionary thinking and to promote creationary truth. Tiles of different shapes and colors appear disconnected when randomly displayed on a surface, but arranged as a mosaic by someone with a purpose, an image may appear which is greater than the sum of individual parts. With purpose in view, the composite chapters of this book are arranged to show that evolutionary thinking is intellectually effete, scientifically vacuous, morally evil, that it is in fact a religious system that should no longer be preached as fact in America's public schools (or in any schools). Some chapters, like blue tiles, may seem different from others, like red ones, but patience in reading may facilitate seeing the beauty and wonder of creation and encourage the rejection of the befuddled alternative.

INTRODUCTION

Jim Remsen, Religion Editor for *The Philadelphia Inquirer*, called in May of 2005 and asked if I knew of someone who would be willing to debate a biology professor on the subject of intelligent design vs. evolution. I offered myself. The debate took place in a conference room on May 13, 2005 at Drexel University, and an article appeared in the Sunday edition, May 29, 2005.[3] Dr. Stacey Ake was my evolutionary opponent.

The article mentioned that I directed Skilton House Ministries (Philadelphia) "which organizes 'released time' religious instruction for Philadelphia public school students."[4] This occurs during regular school hours, and science which supports the doctrine of creation may be taught.

The article quoted me as saying, "I believe a strong case could be made that Darwinism or evolutionism actually is a religion in the guise of science. It wants to force a naturalistic understanding of all scientific endeavor, excluding all supernatural."

My opponent did more or less affirm that the God-notion should be no part of science but seemed unaware that this was essentially religious atheism. Such should never be promoted in America's public schools, but it is.

This photograph of Stacey Ake, Paul Humber, and *Inquirer* reporter Jim Remsen was taken by an *Inquirer* photographer on Paul Humber's camera with the tacit approval of all parties. Other pictures were taken by the same person on a different camera and published in the newspaper.

At one point, my opponent asked, "My question is, when we finally come down to the battle of creation sciences, will it be the Muslim creation [story] that wins? The Christian creation that wins? The Navaho? The aboriginal? Whose creation wins in creation science?"

My response, as recorded in the article, was as follows: "From the one who conquered death." The resurrection of Jesus Christ is perhaps the best attested fact of history. Even the day of worship was changed from Saturday to Sunday, reflecting this historical truth. Generally, traditions like the Sabbath do not change overnight, but this one did! Does the Koran claim that Mohammed conquered death? What Navaho or aboriginal leader ever claimed to be the Way, the Truth, and the Life? "Christian creation," therefore, should seriously be considered over other options, especially since Roman Catholics and Protestants are united in teaching that Jesus Christ, Who conquered death, was actually present at creation, being the very Creator Himself (Heb. 1:8-10)!

I was also recorded as saying, "The genetic code is just screaming intelligent design. They say there's more information in one cell than a whole encyclopedia. It didn't just happen. Someone put the encyclopedia together, and someone put the DNA together."

At another point, I added, "One of the things I have found interesting is how very faithful the Bible is to anticipating modern science. George Washington, the science of his day said if you had bad blood, you have to drain the blood. (I may not have said that this was part of the reason why our first president died, but George Washington was bled and died.) And in Leviticus, it says the life of the flesh is in the blood. Now, how does man know that? Well, it's revealed."

There are many other aspects of biblical revelation which harmonize with scientific truth such as good hygiene practices, giving farm land rest, the hydrological cycles, and ecology (cf., for example, the Deuteronomy 22:6 injunction against harming a mother bird on her nest[5]).

My opponent interjected, "Biology ends where theology begins."

I responded, "But Darwinism is theology. ... We are playing a game of understanding the universe without God. To say this is the only game that you do in science [and] if you do bring in God, we're going to flunk you." Expanding somewhat, Darwin's only degree was in theology, yet he is viewed as being a great scientist. Many scientists today have no problem admiring the wonders of God's creation, but, having said this, there are also many professors today who will degrade (or even fail) students who try to view science within a creationary framework.

Later in the article, I am recorded as saying: "What is covered in the Bible is an intolerance of the notion that the earth has been around in its present form for five billion years or whatever because Jesus put Adam and Eve at the beginning of creation, not long after the beginning. And secondly, the law given to Moses says in six days the

Lord made the heavens and the earth and rested on the seventh. ... I believe recent discoveries have it that there is no animal that has left a fossil remain where there is not some residual Carbon-14 remaining. If they died sixty five to seventy million years ago, there should be no residual carbon left beyond sixty thousand years, and yet in all of these bones there is."

Expanding on the above, I add the following: During my twenty-four year stay as an educator at the Haverford School, I taught that the half-life of ^{14}C is 5730 years. Thirty-five of these take us back two hundred thousand years, and there should not be any detectable ^{14}C left after that period of time. When "tested by highly sensitive accelerator mass spectrometer (AMS) methods, organic samples from every portion of the Phanerozoic record display ^{14}C/C ratios far above the AMS detection threshold of 0.001 percent modern carbon (pmc)."[6] Samples included such things as whale bone, anthracite, coal, fossil wood, petroleum—assumed by evolutionists to be ^{14}C 'dead'.[7] The AMS measurements are consistent with a much younger earth that experienced a global cataclysm that destroyed most of the air-breathing life on the planet less than 20,000 years ago.

New Perspectives

The Statement of Purpose spoke of different tiles in a mosaic. Here is a different piece adjoining the above. My *Inquirer* debater did not seem positively affected by my conversation with her, but sometimes educated people can gain new perspectives. Early in 2005, I sent a number of e-mails to a "Distinguished Professor of Human Genetics and Psychiatry" at a university shool of medicine. In one of the e-mails, he wrote, "I do appreciate this conversation ... I think you have helped me start to think through some significant issues that I had not really seen in quite the same way before."

What I sent this gentleman was from an article I had written a decade prior, while teaching on the faculty of the Haverford School. I had had the privilege of serving as an Advanced Placement Coordinator for the school. The piece I prepared was for *The Index* (a school publication). It exposed significant areas of weakness in evolutionary theory as explained in textbooks used.[8] What follows is the substance of that article, some of which was received by the "Distinguished Professor" who seemed, as admitted above, to gain new perspectives.

First, I explained in the school article that I had received from the College Entrance Examination Board (CEEB) various Advanced Placement course description(s). Biology was included. Apparently, 8 percent of the biology exam was on evolution, and "Evidence for Evolution" was one of the six rubrics under the heading.

Being an evolutionary skeptic, I looked through Neil A. Campbell's textbook, *Biology*, (2nd ed.), the one used at the school the previous year. I also consulted *Life: The Science of Biology* by Purves, Orians, and Heller, the current year's textbook. Both were listed by CEEB as acceptable.

Campbell's book purported to be scientific but stepped over scientific boundaries to metaphysics. It labeled as "myth" the notion "that organic molecules are products of supernatural vital forces" (p. 17) and affirmed the notion "that life developed on earth from nonliving materials" (p. 513). It said, "The history of life is not a story of immutable species individually created on a conservative planet" (p. 9). These statements, however, could not and cannot be supported by science. No human scientist was present in the beginning, and no modern scientist can replicate anything that comes near to the creation of life from inorganic materials. Even if he or she could, it would point in the direction of intelligence being required rather than randomness.

The textbook was inconsistent. It listed as one of the properties of life the "axiom known as biogenesis" ("Life comes only from life," p. 4). If life comes only from life, I asked, how can the author of the text say that "life developed...from nonliving materials" and imply that "supernatural vital forces" should be excluded?

The second textbook was more guarded: "The initial energy source for life's evolution is not known, but volcanic vents were probably important sites for the evolution of proto life" (p. 397).

I was appalled that one of the greatest biologists of all time, Louis Pasteur, was excluded from the twenty-four paged index of Campbell's text. He established the Law of Biogenesis (referred to above) and perhaps should be regarded as the father of modern bacteriology as well as being a major contributor to the developments of vaccination and immunization. He contributed more to world health than perhaps any other modern scientists. Since Campbell's textbook worshipped the notion of evolution ("the one biological theme that unifies all others: evolution," p. 117), one wonders if Pasteur was excluded from the index (downplaying his contribution) because he demolished the prevalent and naive evolutionary notion of spontaneous generation. The current textbook described him as "the great French scientist" and credited him with obtaining "results that finally convinced most people that spontaneous generation does not occur." Authors Purves, Orians, and Heller were apparently not among the "most," however, because their text went on to assert that "life did arise by ... a form of spontaneous generation--under conditions much different from today's" (p. 397).

Pasteur himself was opposed by the biological establishment of his day, and it seems that resistance was/is continuing. Many godless Russians, however, came to the realization that life could only come from a living Source beyond the purview of "science" (narrowly defined) and in harmony with Pasteur's results.

The evidence for evolution given in Campbell's textbook (pp. 434-437) was extremely weak. They included conjectures about biological distributions, misleading information about fossils, arguments from taxonomy, comparative anatomy, embryology, and molecular biology.

Regarding fossils, the text said that the "record of past life is incomplete even today, although ... many of the key links are no longer missing" (p. 435). The only example in context, however, was archaeopteryx, and we have known about that extinct animal for many decades; moreover, fossils of birds predating archaeopteryx have been uncovered, disqualifying archaeopteryx as a "key" link.

Niles Eldredge, interviewed earlier in the text, referred to "the fundamental observation that there are few good examples of slow, steady, gradual transformations within species in the fossil record through time" (p. 421) and added that "a hundred years (after Darwin) there still weren't many satisfying examples of gradual transformations." How would this harmonize with the statement quoted above, "many of the key links are no longer missing?"

In conclusion, metaphysical evolution presuppositionally rules God out of the picture, as I reiterated in my debate with Dr. Stacy (above), and the manifold wisdom and design we see all through creation was/is offered as the product of blind chance. The notion that a computer could have come into existence without intelligence, however, is absurd. How much more the human brain!

"Evolution should not be taught to students unchallenged," I wrote, "at least in science!" Argument against its validity should be encouraged and alternative approaches considered. Moreover, this approach should not be viewed as being inimical to science. Sir Isaac Newton, perhaps the greatest of all modem scientists (gravitation, laws of motion, calculus), had no problem with the concept of God. In his *Principia*, he wrote of the "Lord over all."

Many other scientists, including Robert Boyle (regarded as the father of modern chemistry and an apologist for theism), George Cuvier (credited with being the founder of the science of comparative anatomy), Michael E. DeBakey (famed heart surgeon who said, "I still have almost a religious sense when I work on the heart. It is something God makes."), John Ambrose Fleming (considered the father of modem electronics and first president of the Evolution Protest Movement), Johann Kepler (viewed as the founder of physical astronomy, the one who thought "God's thoughts after Him"), Carolus Linneaus (judged to be the father of biological taxonomy, relating "species" and "kinds"), Joseph Maxwell (also one of the greatest of modern scientists and strong opponent of evolution), Gregory Mendel (the father of genetics and one who rejected Darwin's evolutionary notions), Samuel F. B. Morse (telegraphed, "What hath God wrought!"), John Ray (referred to as the father of English natural history and author of *The Wisdom of God Manifested in the Works of Creation*), and many others likely would have concurred.[9]

To the question, "What other forces do you see leading to the humane holocaust?" Malcolm Muggeridge responded: "I think that after the story's told, when the history of our time is written, we will see that the theory of evolution–which has invaded every single discipline within the whole structure of Western thought which is itself based upon this theory–was one of the most brilliant coups of the devil's. Of course it's complete nonsense, but it has captivated the Western mind. The belief that this theory is absolutely true is so borne in upon the educated that you can't reach them. I find it incredible" (*SCP Journal*, Vol.16:2, 1991, p. 37).

Some years prior to the writing of my school article, I received in my Haverford School mailbox a personal letter from the then Surgeon General, C. Everett Koop, MD. He wrote, "It has been my conviction for many years that evolution is impossible, just on the basis of mathematics alone."

The final paragraph in my article read as follows: "I agree. As far as I am concerned, students would make better use of their time if they were required also to know the evidence against evolution. The biological establishment, I believe, opposes this, but considering opposing evidence is good science."

Chapter 1

. . . .

INTERACTION WITH
EVOLUTIONISTS

C apitalizing the first two letters in the term, "IDiots,"
may seem cute, but it demeans proponents of Intelligent Design (ID). I saw the term used recently.
Earlier, Dr. Richard Dawkins of Oxford University had
described persons like me as "Rome-deniers... nutters...
wingnuts... (they resemble) Holocaust-deniers... (they)
promote... inanities... they deny... the unassailable evidence for biological evolution.... Ignorant, closed-minded,
false teachers... come as close as I can reckon to committing
true sacrilege."[10]

**How Should People of Faith Respond to Ridicule and/or
Intimidation?**

A few years ago, I confronted Dr. Dawkins directly concerning his own foibles (he apologized twice, cf. Chapter
Eight), but is it wise for me to suggest that others follow in
a similar path? I think so, but not because I think I am so
wonderful. I am very limited, but let me refer to a few experiences I have had in confronting the lie of evolution.

In 2001, I moderated two creation/evolution debates, featuring evolutionists (one from the University of Pennsylvania and the other from Temple University). In fact, I am the one who initiated contact with both, had lunch with both, and set up the parameters of the debates with both. (For a fuller account of what happened in the first of these two debaters, see chapter twenty-one.)

Some might question how can anyone so obviously antagonistic toward evolution even consider moderating debates involving two evolutionists? There are three answers.

First, one can have concern and love for an evolutionist, even if he holds to erroneous views. I have already referred to one such contact that concluded rather positively (cf. Introduction). I also have since debated against Evolutionist Brian Richmond of George Washington University's Anthro-

pology Department, and we have carried on cordial correspondence since.

Second, the second of the two debates (not reported in this book) went rather well and is available for purchase. The reader is invited to judge for himself if I was balanced in moderating.

Creationist Paul Humber is seen here with Evolutionist Brian Richmond debating "Should Public Schools Include Only Science that Supports Evolution or Also Include Science that Refutes Evolution?"

Third, the National Center for Science Education puts out REPORTS.

Both the Center and its Journal seek to "promote" evolutionary science, but my name appears appreciatively in one issue of this evolutionary publication.[11] In other words, I was (and am) willing to lend my name to something being published that is on the side of truth—even if appearing in an evolutionary publication. Not everything in *REPORTS* is a lie; the article I was supporting was a needed corrective. (I also have had considerable interaction with Dr. Andrew J. Petto, Editor, National Center for Science Education, and the exchanges have been cordial.)

Big Heads?

David R. Dennis was my tenth grade biology teacher. I would see him during off-class times to talk about evolution. He said that, in the future, we humans would evolve big heads and/or fingers to facilitate the pushing of buttons in the upcoming, automated age. The notion seemed ridiculous to me at the time (and still does), but he and I got along rather well.

Was Hitler a Racist?

My twenty-four years on the Haverford School faculty were enriching in many ways. In addition to serving for a time as Advanced Placement Coordinator (cf. Introduction), I had many valuable interactions with peers. One of my collegial friends was a history teacher who regularly fed me newspaper reports about the latest evolutionary "discoveries"—often from the *New York Times*. I appreciated this focused and free sharing. I also gave a number of Upper School assemblies that challenged evolutionary thinking and was invited to share my creationary perspectives in some science classes.

On one occasion, I asked my colleague, Col. Donald G. Brownlow, an authority on Nazi Germany (one who had served during the D-Day invasion), if he thought Hitler's view of the superior race concept was related to an evolutionary way of thinking. At first he denied it, but eventually he started coming around to the view that Hitler was more of an evolutionist than he (my colleague) realized. He supplied me with supporting documentation. I was also able to get a copy of Hitler's book in German and interact with another Haverford colleague who taught German. In time, I put together a paper that has influenced the thinking of many people.[12] It has been translated into various languages. Here it is again with some upgrading:

The Ascent of Racism

Racism has plagued humanity for thousands of years, and it has especially shown its ugly head during the last few centuries. Think of the myriads of Blacks carried from Africa and sold into slavery in the New World and, more recently, of the blatant racism of Nazi Germany. Even today, there are justifiable concerns along these lines. It is easy to condemn the sins of others, but how is it possible, we should ask, that a leader such as Hitler could sway thousands and even millions of intelligent Germans to his cause? It is one thing to say that Hitler was crazy; it is quite something else to affirm that all Germans were crazy along with him.

There is a hypothesis that has not yet adequately been considered. Staunch evolutionist, Sir Arthur Keith claims, "The German Fuhrer . . . consciously sought to make the practice of Germany conform to the theory of evolution."[13] (I was gratified to see this quotation appearing again, as recently as August 2005, in a commentary written by Dr. D. James Kennedy.)[14]

Elsewhere, Keith wrote, "The leader of Germany is an evolutionist, not only in theory, but, as millions know to their cost, in the rigor of its practice. For him, the national 'front' of Europe is also the evolutionary 'front'; he regards

32

himself, and is regarded, as the incarnation of the will of Germany, the purpose of that will being to guide the evolutionary destiny of its people."[15]

Hitler used the German word for evolution (Entwicklung) over and over again in his book[16]. In fact, it is not unreasonable to suppose that the very title itself of Hitler's book *(My Struggle)*, was influenced by Darwin's subtitle, *Struggle for Existence*, and by the German advocate of evolution, Ernst Haeckel, who published a book in 1905, entitled, *Der Kampf um den Entwicklungs-Gedanken (The Struggle over Evolutionary Thinking)*.

In Hitler's *Mein Kampf*, he spoke of "lower human types." He criticized the Jews for bringing "Negroes into the Rhineland" with the aim of "ruining the white race by the necessarily resulting bastardization." He spoke of "monstrosities halfway between man and ape" and lamented the fact of Christians going to "Central Africa" to set up "Negro missions," resulting in the turning of "healthy ... human beings into a rotten brood of bastards."

In his chapter entitled "Nation and Race," Hitler wrote, "The stronger must dominate and not blend with the weaker, thus sacrificing his own greatness. Only the born weakling can view this as cruel, but he, after all, is only a weak and limited man; for if this law did not prevail, any conceivable higher development (*Hoherentwicklung*) of organic living beings would be unthinkable." A few pages later, he said, "Those who want to live, let them fight, and those who do not want to fight in this world of eternal struggle do not deserve to live."[17]

Was Darwin a Racist?

Present-day Darwinists, for the most part, do not want to be identified with racism; so it is no wonder that some of Darwin's statements touching on this area receive little attention. He spoke of the "gorilla" and the "Negro" as occupying evolutionary positions between the "baboon" and the "civilized races of man" ("Caucasian"):

At some future period, not very distant as measured by centuries, the civilized races of man will almost certainly exterminate, and replace, the savage races throughout the world. At the same time, the anthropomorphous apes ... will no doubt be exterminated. The break between man and his nearest allies will then be wider, for it will intervene between man in a more civilized state, as we may hope, even than the Caucasian, and some ape as low as a baboon, instead of as now between the negro [sic] or Australian and the gorilla.[18]

Later in the same volume, Darwin wrote:

It has often been said ... that man can resist with impunity the greatest diversities of climate and other changes; but this is true only of the civilized races. Man in his wild condition seems to be in this respect almost as susceptible as his nearest allies, the anthropoid apes, which have never yet survived long, when removed from their native country.[19]

Referring to *On the Origin of Species*, by Darwin, Harvard University's Stephen Jay Gould wrote, "Biological arguments for racism may have been common before 1859, but they increased by orders of magnitude following the acceptance of evolutionary theory."[20] He cited various sources to support his thesis, but two names which do not appear in his section entitled "Racism" are the names of Edwin G. Conklin and Henry Fairfield Osborn.

Were Some American Biologists Racists?

It is important to recognize that these two men were writing before Hitler's brand of evolution unfolded itself on the European continent. Some of the language of both Conklin and Osborn is reminiscent of Darwin, if not also of Hitler. It is important to keep in mind who these men were. Conklin was professor of biology at Princeton University from 1908 to 1933. He was also President of the American Association for the Advancement of Science in 1936 (the year of Hitler's Berlin Olympics). He wrote: "Comparison of any modern race with the Neanderthal or Heidelberg types shows that all have changed, but probably the negroid races more closely resemble the original stock than the white or yellow races.[21] Every consideration should lead those who believe in the superiority of the white race to strive to preserve its purity and to establish and maintain the segregation of the races, for the longer this is maintained, the greater the preponderance of the white race will be."[22]

Henry Fairfield Osborn was a professor of biology and zoology at Columbia University. For twenty-five years (1908-1933), he was president of the American Museum of Natural History's board of trustees. Osborn wrote: "The negroid stock is even more ancient than the Caucasian and Mongolians, as may be proved by an examination not only of the brain, of the hair, of the bodily characteristics ... but of the instincts, the intelligence. The standard of intelligence of the average adult Negro is similar to that of the eleven-year-old-youth of the species *Homo Sapiens*."[23]

In a book dedicated to John T. Scopes (the evolutionist teacher made famous by the Scopes "monkey trial"), Osborn wrote, "The ethical principle inherent in evolution is that only the best has a right to survive."[24]

In this book, Osborn said that he was summing up an article he had written for the *New York Times* (February 26, 1922). One could speculate that Hitler, himself, might in some way have had access to this teaching prior to his writing of *Mein Kampf*, so similar does this last statement sound to much of what he believed and wrote.

It is easy to believe that Hitler had such an interest in the boxing match between Joe Louis and the German, Max Schmeling, (June 19, 1936). It "was rife with political and racial overtones … "[25] Less than a year prior, Paul Gallico, writer for the New York Daily News, wrote, "Louis, the magnificent animal … He eats. He sleeps. He fights…. Is he all instinct, all animal? Or have a hundred million years left a fold upon his brain? I see in this colored man something so cold, so hard, so cruel that I wonder as to his bravery. Courage in the animal is desperation. Courage in the human is something incalculable and divine."[26]

Did Vestiges of Scientific Racism Continue?

In April of 1986, *The Pennsylvania Gazette* (University of Pennsylvania) published an article featuring a skull labeled "NEGRO/LUNATIC." The caption under the photograph read, "Scientific racism: Skulls like these, housed in the University Museum, were once used to 'prove' white supremacy."[27]

The National Geographic Society, in November of 1985, set before the public a display of four million years of bipedalism in its magazine. Nine hominids, strongly suggestive of evolutionary development, are drawn from Australopithecus-afarensis (a "Lucy" type), through modern Homo sapiens. The first five in the sequence had a darker skin tone; the last four, lighter. The editors acknowledged that the skin color is speculative, but, in the March 1986 issue of *The National Geographic* (Members Forum), they said the following: "Since the three *H. sapiens* variations depicted were based on fossil evidence in Europe, Mr. Matternes gave them a lighter tone."[28]

But this seems to be misleading, since the last *four* in the sequence have the lighter skin tones and the fourth from the end was based on evidence from Kenya, Africa! Could this be an example of a subtle form of racism still affecting the public long after Hitler and World War II?

The Christian, as a follower of Jesus, does not have the option of racism. Jesus was no racist. He told His followers to love our fellow man—even our enemies. He sought to "draw all men" to Himself (John 12:32), and "He made from one, every nation of mankind to live on all the face of the earth" (Acts 17:26, NASV). Jesus' salvation reaches beyond Israel "to the end of the earth" (Isa. 49:6).

Chapter 2

. . . .

WAS MY ARTICLE, TRANSLATED AND PUBLISHED IN VARIOUS LANGUAGES, IN ERROR?

Not everyone who read my *Ascent of Racism* article (Chapter One) appreciated it. One person publicly took me to task. I decided to contact him personally and interact with his thinking. The two words, "liar" and "moron," were applied by him to me. My final communication with him came after his "moron" accusation but prior to his "liar" appellation. With minor adjustments, here is the substance of my concerns expressed to this evolutionist.

First, the evolutionist saw my comparing evolutionists to Hitler as unfair. He wrote, "Don't get all self-righteous on me, Paul. You don't think equating me and other 'evolutionists' with Hitler is a 'put down?'"

I responded with, "Carl Sagan used evolutionary thinking to justify the slaughter of the unborn. According to him, humans go through an evolutionary unfolding during development in the womb. The face of the child, for example, becomes 'reptilian ... [then] somewhat pig-like.' Eventually, it 'resembles a primate's but is still not quite human'" (*Parade Magazine*, April 22, 1990, p. A8).

I continued, "All of this, of course, is nonsense, but it affects gullible people. Six million is the number linked with Hitler, but well over thirty million[29] babies have been slaughtered in American abortuaries since 1973! Yes, Carl Sagan and convoluted evolution are partly to blame, and the entrance of evolutionary thinking into Germany via Ernst Haeckel had an impact on Germans, including Hitler. Ideas have consequences, and faulty 'science' has fostered evil."

Then, reviewing some of our correspondence, I wrote that the original concern I had had with the evolutionist's response to my article was that it blamed ICR for the claim that "Hitler used the German word for evolution (Entwicklung) over and over again in his book." (The evolutionist was actually quoting my words at that point.) My antagonist then added, "Like so many of ICR's claims, this one simply is not true—a quick scan of several online English translations of Mein Kampf shows only one use of the word 'evolution,' in a context which does not refer at all to biological evolution." This claim, however, on the part of the evolutionist, was and is patently false. Here is how I proved my point:

Development = Evolution

When tracing the word "development" in Hitler's Mein Kampf, one finds 159 hits (consistent with my "over and over again" statement objected to be the evolutionist. I am confident that the German word behind these instances is, in many if not most cases, Entwicklung (i.e., evolution) and rather suspect that the translators chose "development" rather than "evolution" because they sought to disconnect Hitler from any association with the widely revered doctrine of evolution. Entwicklung appears many more times than once, and the evolutionist's statement, not mine, was and is false.

The evolutionist did not yield to the above point because he thought all 159 hits were irrelevant to the subject of "biological evolution." It is my purpose, in the paragraph that follows, to show that Hitler was indeed dealing with biological evolution. The following phrases or terms, all from Hitler's *Mein Kampf*, do reveal an evolutionary framework of thinking: nature, preserving, breeding, species, stronger must dominate, higher development, higher breeding, lower colored peoples, struggle, existence, preservation of the species, laws of development, the natural law of all development, victory of the stronger, preservation, higher development of living creatures, life struggles, struggle for existence, scientific knowledge, mankind's struggle for existence, and ruthless application of Nature's stern and rigid laws.

Of course, Hitler was not a biology teacher, but he did see himself as furthering (laudably, in his mind) evolution's supposedly relentless path of weeding out the weak and strengthening the fit. (For contexts of quotations, see Appendix Two.)

Hitler's Bow Before "Nature"

It is not only in *Mein Kampf* that this kind of language was used by Hitler. Here is what he said to officer cadets on June 22, 1944:

> Nature is always teaching us ... that she is governed by the principle of selection: that victory is to the strong and the weak must go to the wall. She teaches us that what may seem cruel to us, because it affects us personally or because we have been brought up in ignorance of her laws, is nevertheless often essential if a higher way of life is to be attained. Nature ... knows nothing of the notion of humanitarianism which signifies that the weak

must at all costs be surrounded and preserved even at the expense of the strong.

Nature does not see in weakness any extenuating reasons ... on the contrary, weakness calls for condemnation .... War is therefore the unalterable law of the whole of life—the prerequisite for the natural selection of the strong and the precedent for the elimination of the weak. What seems cruel to us is from Nature's point of view entirely obvious. A people that cannot assert itself must disappear and another must take its place. All creation is subject to this law; no one can avoid it ... Since life on earth began, struggle has been the very essence of existence ....[30]

(As an aside, Dr. Richard Weikart of the California State University's History Department in Stanislaus, is the author of *From Darwin to Hitler: Evolutionary Ethics, Eugenics, and Racism in Germany*, Palgrave Macmillan, 2004. In response to an e-mail from him, I supplied him with the above quotation, which I do not believe appears in his book. I also gave him the reference, to which he replied with a thank you. On August 19, 2005, he wrote, "I have many quotations by Hitler that say essentially the same thing, and I will use many of them in my forthcoming book, *Hitler's Ethic*. This, therefore, is added confirmation that this matter was not peripheral to Hitler's perverted and evolutionary thinking.)

Resuming with the flow of thought, the evolutionist also expressed himself that Hitler's abuse of evolutionary theory should not disqualify the theory itself. He wrote, "Is it your opinion that Hitler's misuse of evolutionary theory was somehow evolutionary theory's fault, and therefore evolutionary theory is evil?" He then added that Hitler also used God-words in *Mein Kampf*. He was wondering if it was inconsistent for me to cast aspersions on evolutionary theory because of Hitler's evolution-words while not doing the same against Christianity because of Hitler's God-words.

A Deadly Theory

In response, I wrote: "First, it is not my point that Hitler's example disproves evolution. Evolution is false for many reasons, and none of them need be related to Hitler. It is my point that mankind has suffered greatly because the educationally elite have coddled this nonsensical and deadly theory. Hitler was deadly, and abortion is deadly."

I added, "Second, many have tried to condemn Christianity because of misapplications by supposed adherents. Hitler's references in *Mein Kampf* to God or the Almighty probably were more political than heartfelt, for the Scriptures are replete with admonitions to care for the weak and sickly. Evolutionary theory, however, is amoral, and Hitler promoted survival of the fittest ("the weak must go to the wall")—not loving neighbors and being his brother's keeper."

The Bible, in both testaments, makes it very clear that we all came from one set of parents. There is only one race, the human one. We are all sons and daughters of Adam and Eve. Cain slew his brother not because he was of a different race but because of hatred in his heart. Hitler was a sinful egomaniac. He made an idol of himself, the Nazi State, and "survival of the fittest." Sadly, many Germans were duped by his convoluted views, and these views were buttressed by Darwin's (via Haeckel) racist nonsense. Moreover, the Germans were not alone; many Americans, too, were and are duped by the same nonsense.

The evolutionist wrote, "Now please tell me why Herr Hitler keeps talking about this 'Almighty God' in *Mein Kampf.*" I responded:

"The phrase, 'Almighty God,' occurs three times. The name, 'Jesus,' never appears. The word, 'Bible,' never appears. The title, 'Messiah,' never appears, and there is no occurrence of the name, 'Jehovah.'"

Did any Christians in Germany (and Elsewhere) Oppose Hitler's Brand of Evolution?

The response of true Christians to Hitler's perversion of Christianity and the response of evolutionary scientists to Hitler's attempt to force his version of evolution upon Europe contrast markedly. Here are words of Albert Einstein:

> Being a lover of freedom, when the (Nazi) revolution came, I looked to the universities to defend it, knowing that they had always boasted of their devotion to the cause of truth; but no, the universities were immediately silenced. Then I looked to the great editors of the newspapers, whose flaming editorials in days gone by had proclaimed their love of freedom; but they, like the universities, were silenced in a few short weeks ... Only the Church stood squarely across the path of Hitler's campaign for suppressing the truth. I never had any special interest in the Church before, but now I feel a great affection and admiration for it because the Church alone has had the courage and persistence to stand for intellectual and moral freedom. I am forced to confess that what I once despised I now praise unreservedly.[31]

Correspondingly, were there zealous evolutionists who were sent to concentration camps for opposing Hitler? Roland H. Bainton wrote of Christians: "Some four thousand Protestant ministers led by Karl Barth and Hans Asmussen formed the Confessing Church, which at Barmen in 1934 declared that no human Fuhrer could stand above the Word of God. The Confessing Church lost its properties, its seminary was suppressed, its journals were prohibited, and when war came, the members of its clergy of military age and not in prison were assigned to positions of greatest danger, while the older leaders were sent to concentration camps. Among them was Martin Niemoller, a Lutheran pastor who after more than half a year in solitary confinement was brought to trial under Hitler's law against 'treacherous attacks upon state and party.' His refusal to capitulate and his persistent resistance to Nazism made him the symbolic figure of the Protestant opposition until the downfall of the Nazis."[32]

Caring for Neighbors vs. Killing Them for Survival

The evolutionist did not comment on the memorandum submitted to Hitler on June 4, 1936. The German Evangelical Church had questioned whether the Chancellor was trying "to dechristianize the German people." Continuing with the memorandum, "When, within the compass of the National Socialist view of life, an anti-Semitism is forced on the Christian that binds him to hatred of the Jew, the Christian injunction to love one's neighbor still stands, for him, opposed to it" (see again footnote 31).

Weapons of the Spirit, shown on PBS-TV, recounted the fact that five thousand Protestants of Le Chambon, France, rescued five thousand Jews because they knew they were to love their neighbors. Another more recent PBS documentary featured Dietrich Bonhoeffer's opposition to Hitler, and

The New York Times reported the death of Victor Kugler in 1981. It credited him as the one who "hid Anne Frank" in Holland.[33] The article describes him as a "Christian."

Corrie ten Boom, her sister, brother, and father, all also of Holland and sincere Christians, were imprisoned (some died) in Ravensbruck because they, too, were shielding Jews from Nazi persecution. They did not believe, with Hitler, that war was "the unalterable law of the whole of life—the prerequisite for the natural selection of the strong and the precedent for the elimination of the weak." There were Christians in Poland whose hearts went out to Jews. Nechama Tec, a professor of sociology at the University of Connecticut, herself a beneficiary for three years of Christian compassion in Poland, wrote a book, *When Light Pierced the Darkness*.[34] Her thesis was/is that religion played a very important role in motivating Christians to compassion for the Jews. The religion of evolution, however, played a very important role in motivating Nazis to exterminate Jews.

Jews have established a foundation for righteous Christians, headed by Rabbi Harold Schulweis? It was/is called the Foundation to Sustain the Righteous Christians. Israel apparently had at least thirty-one persons who received pensions from the National Insurance Foundation. It also allowed Rose Warmer to distribute New Testaments to schools nationally because she "voluntarily went to the infamous Auschwitz death camp during World War II."

For my part, my only hope is in the perfect righteousness of the Savior, Creator Christ. I reflect, also, with hope on the renewed beauty of people like those of Le Chambon who reached out in love to oppressed Jews because they wanted to obey Jesus.

I concluded my correspondence with the evolutionist with these words: "May the same God who gave grace to the people of Le Chambon continue to touch your life with gladness and love, Paul."

Following my correspondence (partially reproduced above), this same evolutionist wrote, "Don't write to me any more, liar." Adjusting the tile metaphor of the Purpose Statement somewhat, one could consider this chapter like a tile resisting intense heat on a returning space shuttle. Being called a moron and a liar is not enjoyable, but the Apostle Peter exhorted us to be ready to give an answer to anyone who asks us a reason for our hope with meekness and fear (1 Peter 3:15). On the surface, it does not appear that my answer was very effective for the evolutionist, but another apostle did not convert immediately at the testimony of Stephen, either. We serve a God of hope.

Chapter 3

. . . .

SCIENTIFIC EVIDENCE FOR CREATION

Returning to the tiles/mosaic metaphor, this chapter may be thought of as twenty-five mini-tiles, all designed to show the superiority of creation science over evolution. A number of colleagues helped me with what follows.[35] I served as editor.

We hear in the secular media as well as in many non-Christian religious arenas that man is basically good and that this good can be encouraged and promoted until the world is at peace. This point of view denies the message of the Bible that we are people in rebellion against God.

Increasingly, the idea of secular humanism, that man is the ultimate determiner of right and truth, is being taught in the media, our public schools, and even in some churches claiming to be Christian. Along with this approach, we then find that abortion becomes a "right" for a woman, and even that religious objections to this are said to be based on religious myths and outdated ideas.

The religiously believed philosophy of evolutionism, the idea that all forms of life on earth are the result of changes happening to an original cell which just happened to come together to form life, is a central tenet of secular humanism. Evolutionary ideas stretch beyond the origin of life and its many variations, declaring the universe itself originated in an unexplained sudden expansion billions of years ago, and that this sudden expansion resulted in galaxies, including our own, and eventually resulted in life itself. Thus, even our consciousness and our ideas of right and wrong, good and evil, are said to be the result of an accident, or series of accidents, which took place over enormous amounts of time. This not only denies the God of the Bible and the messages of creation and redemption and accountability to Him, it denies any supernatural intelligence at all.

Theistic evolutionists try to combine humanistic science and what God says. They say God "did it through evolution." God certainly could have done it that way, but the fact is that He says He did not. Genesis records six days of creation, of various "kinds" of life being created supernaturally and separately and only being able to reproduce "after their own kinds." The two ideas, evolution and creation by God, are at odds with each other. In order to intermingle them, you must fudge important aspects of one and/or the other. Thus, theistic evolutionists find themselves in a position of needing to believe current science to an extent that requires ignoring or reinterpreting God's Word, the Bible.

In order to help those who wisely believe that God knows how to communicate and means what He says, the following twenty-five points may be noted about creation and evolution. They offer a brief overview of the listed topics, not a detailed explanation. Also, the number of topics could be expanded.

1. Either matter was created or it is eternal. Christians believe God created matter. Humanists believe that matter, after evolving its own intelligence, "created"

God. Any argument against one of these two views is an argument for the other. Similarly, creation itself is either the result of intelligence or it is not. The theory of evolution argues for a non-intelligent cause and process. Creation, in any form (there are non-Christian forms of creation beliefs), argues for an intelligent cause and process.

2. Which came first, the chicken or the egg? Did you know that the answer to the question poses a problem for evolutionists? If the egg came first, then it could not have been a fertilized one. (You may be unaware that eggs you buy in the store are not fertilized and would never hatch chickens; roosters, which are needed to provide sperm cells, are kept away from the hens.) Under normal circumstances, hens store sperm cells from the rooster internally to fertilize an egg before the shell is formed. Now if the egg came first, there would have been no rooster to provide sperm, nor hen to store it. Therefore, both the chicken and the rooster came first, and they had to be fully functional to produce eggs and, after hatching, chicks. The evolutionist cannot move backward, in a reductionist fashion, to diminish this complexity to something less but still functional. The creationist, on the other hand, sees the complexity of roosters and hens and rightly concludes that these marvelous creatures were created together in the beginning. The computer you use was obviously designed by someone, even though you may never have seen him or her. Living roosters and hens are far more complex than any inanimate computer.

3. The fossil record is a record of things that died. Relationships between fossils are based on the idea that either they are so close to being alike that we believe they were the same sort of plant or animal or else based on ideas about the relationships which determine the conclusions. We often read about this or that transitional (in between) form bridging the gap between one kind of life and another. It is important to remember that the transitional forms found are only transitional because they are declared to be. We have no evidence that they are not simply another "kind" of plant or animal. For instance, if someone who had never seen a bat saw a fossil of one, it might easily be declared that this was a transitional form between birds and mammals. But we, knowing what bats are, know they are a kind of animal unto themselves, and not a transitional form. The same thing happens with fossils. We see them declared "transitional" between birds and dinosaurs or between fish and reptiles. The reality is that a "transitional" form, like beauty, is in the eye of the beholder. People tend to see what they want to see, and the theory of evolution demands transitional forms. Thus some discoveries are declared transitional and heralded loudly in the press. When the idea of transitional is retracted, however, it is often done very quietly, with little or no press coverage. We and the scientists themselves, are left with the impression that great many transitional forms have been found. The truth is far different.[36]

Before going on to the next mini-tile, I share a perspective from Dr. Duane T. Gish, who wrote in a personal letter to me the following: "I would like to suggest that you add more to what you have on the fossil record, the major features of which not only are contradictory to evolution but which are actually incompatible with evolution. I am enclosing a copy of my book *Evolution: the Fossils STILL Say No!* You will find this to be a rich source on the fossil record."

I wholeheartedly agree with Dr. Gish that more could be said here about the incompatibility of fossils evidence with evolution. I also highly recommend his excellent book. The purpose of this present book, however, is not to duplicate what is well documented elsewhere. The reader should understand, nevertheless, that the fossil record points to catastrophic deposition of animals in water events, many of which were associated in one way or another with a flood during the time of our forefather, Noah.

4. The fossil record also reveals distinct kinds of plants and animals with no evolutionary connection to each other. Because of these gaps in the fossil record, there have been a number of theories proposed to explain them while still holding to evolution. "Punctuated equilibrium" is the idea that evolutionary changes happened in small, isolated populations very quickly and left no fossil record. The fossil record itself, however, is very much in accord with what we read in the Bible: plants and animals were created by "kind."[37]

5. Evolutionists must declare that the earliest life forms were quite simple and that time and some mysterious evolutionary process led to the complexity and variety we see on the earth today. The fact of the matter is, however, that this thought of "simple to complex" is the product either of ignorance or a deliberate at-

tempt to deceive. Darwin considered the cell to be a sort of little blob. The more we learn about the cell, however, the more incredibly complex it is seen to be. Thousands of proteins interact in specific and orderly ways in a protected environment. Nutrients are taken in, broken down, used, and waste expelled; there are reactions to the environment and then the cell duplicates itself in a chain of events we still do not completely understand. There is nothing simple about a cell. There was nothing simple about any cell at any time. And yet a cell is the simplest form of life we can find! So the idea of "simple to complex" in an evolutionary time scale is denied by the complexity of the individual cell itself.

6. Evolutionists sometimes try to go in the opposite direction; they will speak of the complexity of a snow flake or a tornado. Biologically speaking, there is a huge difference between the complexity of a cellular system and the complexity of a snow flake or a tornado. This is an area of potential confusion that evolutionists have found they can readily exploit if they use enough fancy sounding words and pretend that the same natural process that formed a snow flake could form a cell. Snow flakes can not take in nutrients, break them down, use them, or intelligently expel them. All cells can. Snow flakes are beautiful, but they are not living nor anywhere near as complex as cells.

7. Many illustrations of human "evolution" showed the darker-skinned people as emerging from the ape line first and the lighter-skinned humans being the actual final products of evolution.[38] In line with

this reasoning, evolution can be held responsible for many of the horrors of racist ideas which existed in the late nineteenth, into the twentieth centuries, and even until now. It was not so long ago that the dark-skinned folk were considered not yet fully human in the evolutionary sequence. We have already seen (chapter one) that Hitler adopted evolutionary ideas to support genocide and the concept of the promotion of a superior (white) race of men and women, but as real science has discovered that all humans are genetically the same species, and that all can successfully marry and have children across racial lines, evolutionists have backed off of the idea that skin color determines how far up or down the evolutionary ladder one might be. This is also their conclusion based on the need for political correctness.[39]

1874 Racism: Haechel's Anthropogenie
Notice that it is an African who is placed in a tree with apes.

8. Evolutionists have attempted to prove their case by mixing up two different processes under the term of "evolution." The first is variation. We see variation every day. Puppies and kittens are all born with individual differences in their coloring and personalities. In fact, we know that sometimes these differences can be huge, for examples both Chihuahuas and Great Danes are dogs. Would someone looking at the fossil record think that? Or that they lived at the same time? Perhaps not. But they are both varieties of dog. We can see some remarkable variations in certain kinds of things, but we still recognize them as the kind of thing they are, be they dogs, horses, cats, or people. We know Pygmies, Zulus, Germans, and Chinese are all human beings, just different varieties. Because the word "evolution" simply means change, the evolutionists point to these variations within kind and claim that this proves the theory of evolution that posits changes far beyond the Genesis "kinds." But evolution of one kind to another, such as the evolution (so it is claimed) of fish to human, requires a whole lot more than variation. It requires massive changes in body type and behaviors. It is a false argument to take the small variations we see on a daily basis and claim this proves the evolution of a one-celled organism into ferns and people and elephants and butterflies and oak trees. Many evolutionists must surely know this, but they refuse to submit to its truth.

9. The theory of evolution depends on four things being true: enormous amounts of time, fortuitous chances, beneficial mutations, and natural selection. None of these four supports evolution at all:

Time tears things down; it does not build things up. If you leave a bicycle out in the weather, it rusts and falls apart--it does not become an automobile.

Chance is an argument proven wrong time and again. There is no chance in the world or the universe or all time that something as complex as the "simple" cell could have evolved chemically. There is no chance mathematically or in any lab that life evolved accidentally. All efforts to get life to just happen with the right combination of chemicals and circumstances have resulted in utter failure.

Mutations, or changes in the genetic structures of plants and animals, especially with respect to the higher order of animals, are almost always detrimental and often lethal. While some mutations (especially in the plant and microbial world) may prove beneficial under certain conditions, changing those conditions usually renders the benefit almost useless. In fact, populations of organisms often oscillate between various forms as environmental conditions change, a wonderful testimony to the adaptive design within all living things. In general, those mutations that remain in the genetic structure represent one of two things: accidental duplications of material or losses of material. In no case has any increase of information naturally added to the cell ever been observed to produce a new form or function. The idea that this not only happened once but consistently throughout the imagined billion years to turn a single-celled organism into you is, however, required by evolution.

Natural selection fits very nicely within a creation model. What Darwin did was assume that this "selection" process would drive a "building" process, where organisms that did not possess the ability to walk would be pressured into developing such ability or where organisms that did not posses the ability to fly would be pressured into developing that ability. As such, natural selection was given a capability it never did posses, the ability to generate or create something. All natural selection can do is select among the features that are already present in the biological world. It acts as a weeding-out system, not a developing system. If enough genetic information is eliminated from the gene pool, a new trait or feature may emerge (e.g. dog breeds), but this is only if such features and traits were within the gene pool initially. These notions were published by creationist William Blyth prior to Charles Darwin's promotion.[40]

10. There is strong evidence being brought forward that some things presumed as being millions of years old by evolutionists are not that old. One good example is dinosaur bones. Some of them show strong evidence of not being very old at all; they have not degenerated enough to be millions of years old. (See chapter nineteen of this book.)

11. Many life forms, once thought extinct by evolutionists, have been found alive, healthy today, and unchanged. Coelacanths, for example, were thought to have become extinct sixty million years ago, but they live today! Another example is the Wollemi pines in Australia, which appear to be genetic clones of each

other. Evolutionists scramble quickly to invent new explanations. Under the guise of "science always corrects itself," they have to resort to ever more inventive explanations to keep evolution alive despite the mounting evidence against it. So what we end up with is the explanation that while some populations of Coelacanth survived unchanged, others, in other environments, changed drastically and evolved into other forms of life. The lack of genetic changes in the Wollemi pines, which are supposed to be millions of years old as a species, has no evolutionary explanation.

12. It is a general observation that all non-living things tend to degenerate, but this is also true of living systems. At best, they fulfill the potential of the code passed down to them from their ancestors and then age or succumb to attack, accident, disease, or accumulated injuries. This supports the concept that everything is on a general path of degeneration from a higher state of organization provided by an act of intelligent creation. Degeneration and evolutionary advances are opposing concepts.

13. The Neanderthal is often presented as a pre-human creature; however, there is evidence that some Neanderthals were humans who lived much longer than modern humans do. The aging process may account for morphological changes in bone structure, etc. Their brains were as large, or larger, than ours, and the evidence of their lives being intelligent is showing up in a variety of places. It might also be pointed out that the book of Job describes humans who lived in very difficult circumstances and dwelt

in caves at least part of the time (Job 24:2-12 and Job 30:1-8).[41]

14. The idea of a conflict between religion and science is a product of the evolutionary mind. There is no conflict between the facts of nature and the revealed truth of the Bible. The conflict arises from the evolutionary interpretation of nature and its facts, an interpretation designed to eliminate the need for God and to relegate Him either to non-existence or to impotence after the first moment of creation. Contrary to this assertion of all being able to progress without a God, the design and complexity of everything we see in creation cries out, as Paul wrote to the Romans, about not only the reality of God, but about His eternal power and divine nature, which many choose to ignore, preferring a lie ("For although they knew God, they neither glorified Him as God nor gave thanks to Him, but their thinking became futile and their foolish hearts were darkened;" Romans 1:18). Moreover, many of the founders of the scientific disciplines we are involved with today were Christian creationists not just by default, but as devoted believers. There are many scientists today who also are Christian creationists, contrary to what the evolutionists would have us believe.

15. The long ages of the universe and the earth are often presented as proved by radiometric dating. Radiometric dating depends on three assumptions being true: that the original amounts of both mother and daughter elements are known (and this can often be mathematically determined, so is less challenged

than the next two); that the rate of decay has been constant through time; and that there has been no migration of elements into or out of the samples being tested. Both of the second assumptions are false and known to be false. Rates of decay can vary widely for a number of reasons, and the migration of elements into and out of rocks is also known. Life forms are often dated by radiocarbon dating, which is beset with even more known false assumptions which invalidate it beyond a short range of dates. In summary, radiometric dating, while able to present some evidence for some things, is not the reliable marker of age that evolutionary science would like us to believe it is.[42]

16. Science traditionally is the knowledge and study of that which can be discovered and worked with by man (natural phenomena). It is difficult to know how to deal with the non-natural. There have been attempts to discern the benefits of prayer on healing, but in general, science had two choices: (1) to admit that limitations exist and that science finds it difficult to measure the supernatural or (2) to deny even the possibility of causes or influences which are not natural. Science today, for the most part, has chosen the second option, essentially denying that there are any supernatural causes or influences outside of nature itself which affect nature, but this is irrational. If we see a painting of a flower, we know there was a painter who painted it. Evolutionary science, however, denies any supernatural agency could have formed the actual flower that exists in a form that is much more detailed and complex than a painting could ever be. Rationality would demand

that if the painting had a painter, the actual flower must have had a Creator/Designer. Similarly, we can play with a gyroscope or examine a globe of the world and recognize that both these things are the products of intelligent design, but then some turn to the beauty of the galaxies, the complexity of our solar system, or the design of our earth and declare them all the products of time and evolutionary events without any intelligence being involved at all. This is irrational thinking.

17. Evolutionary geologists see rock layers as taking long ages to form. The earth's entire rock sequences thus, according to them, took millions or even billions of years to form. Yet it is now increasingly acknowledged that catastrophic events formed much of the earth's rock layers. Much of geologic time is now reckoned as shown in the bedding planes between the layers. Nevertheless, evolutionists still cling to the idea of an ancient earth.[43]

18. The presence of two different sexes is a puzzle for evolutionists. Single-celled organisms reproduce by dividing themselves or budding off of themselves. Each "daughter" is exactly like the "mother." So where did the male/female difference come from? Genetically, this male/female difference helps control–usually by elimination–the presence of persistent mutations in a population, the very mutations needed for evolution to continue. So the advent of sexual reproduction evolutionarily is a real bugaboo for the evolutionists and something they cannot explain. The Bible is clear that human beings were made male and female from the beginning, and

although it may not state explicitly the same for animals, the fact that these animals are recognized as beasts and birds and fish from the beginning is a strong indication that they were also male and female from the beginning.

19. When we look at nature, we see, no matter what part of the world we are in, truly complex relationships among various living things: plants require insects for fertilization; animal populations are kept in check by a predator/prey relationship, ants "farm" and "milk" aphids which live on plants. Food chains are not simple chains but can be very complex. Some life forms are parasitic of others, and some depend on others for their existence even though they are not parasites. Evolution declares these complex series of relationships developed accidentally through time. Rational thought, however, is enough to deny this, for the members involved in a complex series of intricate relationships must all be there from the start for those relationships to exist.

20. All cells are made up of huge molecules, and these molecules are made up of long strings of amino acids, sugars, and other small molecules. There are different ways that amino acids can be formed, and there are different ways sugars can be formed. However, all living things require a special form of amino acid called "left-handed" and a special form of sugar called "right-handed." In nature, both right and left handed amino acids and sugars are formed. Yet, let one right-handed amino acid into a cell and it is like throwing in a backward gear. Evolutionary thinking declares that these left-handed amino acids

and right-handed sugars came together fortuitously through time to form life. There are two enormous problems with this. First, there is no known reason for this to have happened or known environment in which it could have happened. Second, life is not simply the right chemicals at the right time and place. Life is a series of processes in which chemicals are involved. This series of processes, by its very nature, is strong evidence that living things were formed as an act of intelligent creation.

21. The structure of the universe is such that astrophysicists have difficulty believing it could have evolved. In 1989, a structure was found to be so enormous that it is five thousand times wider than our galaxy, the Milky Way. This structure, called The Great Galactic Wall by Margaret J. Geller and John P. Huchra of the Harvard-Smithsonian Center for Astrophysics, is too big to fit into the evolutionary scheme of things. According to *Science* (November 11, 1989), the wall is so large and massive, that it could not have been built by gravitational attraction during the supposed fifteen billion year age of the universe. Then, in 1990, a survey, involving the Kitt Peak National Observatory in Arizona and the Anglo Australian Observatory in Australia, found that this structure was one of seven great galactic walls, making the total structure thirty thousand times larger than the Milky Way.[44]

22. Mutations can give bacteria a resistance to certain types of antibiotics. As such, evolutionists have frequently pointed to this phenomenon as a means of "seeing evolution in a Petri dish." However, analyses

of the mutations that produce this resistance suggest a much different conclusion. Instead, these mutations reduce or eliminate the binding affinity, regulatory function, and transport capacity of certain proteins. While these mutations provide the bacterium a resistance to certain antibiotics, they do so at the expense of these cellular functions. Such mutations clearly provide variation within the bacterial population, and as such, fit nicely within a creation model. However, evolution claims to be an explanation for the origin of biological functions. Mutations that reduce or eliminate cellular functions cannot be offered as examples of how those functions "evolved." In fact, such mutations are the exact opposite of that required by evolution.

23. In 1848, apparently 98 percent of peppered moths in Britain were gray, the rest being black. When the Industrial Revolution put a lot of soot on the trees, being light colored was a liability to moths that lived on tree trunks. Birds could see and eat them, and within fifty years, the population of gray moths went down to 5 percent. Then air pollution laws cleaned things up, and gray once again predominated. This, however, is variation within species (a nice example of change in gene frequency)—not evolution. No new organism came into existence. There were gray and black varieties in 1848, and there are gray and black varieties today. More recently, this study has been challenged. First, the moths do not generally position themselves on tree trunks. Second, the pictures of moths on tree trunks in books were artificially fastened there for photographing.

24. Evolutionists boast that evolution is more than a theory, saying even that it is a proven fact! This is hubris, delusion, or a lie. Evolution is a mere presupposition; it hardly qualifies even as a theory. It certainly is not a proven fact. Think for a moment about UFOs. Some may believe that LGM (little green men) are physically abducting people from the desert and transporting them elsewhere. If billions of dollars were being spent to promote this notion as verifiable science and most respected academicians were teaching it as truth, then it would not be surprising, given the dynamics of social peer pressure, that many people would adopt the UFO notion as true science. An irony exists, however. It is this. Even with the tremendous efforts of many academicians promoting evolution and scorning the Bible, many Americans (referring to both continents) still are not persuaded of the evolutionary "presupposition."

25. A foundation of biology is life comes only from life. Biologists have never observed a single exception to this truth; it is called the Biogenetic Law. Prior to the germ theory of disease proposed by Ignatz Semmelweis and finally accepted under Louis Pasteur in 1864, it was believed that organisms generated spontaneously from nonliving matter. This was called spontaneous generation and accounts for the popularity of Darwin's *Origin of Species* (first published in 1859). Pasteur's germ theory has never been shown to have any exceptions, however, and no method is known by which life could have arisen from non-life. Humanistic evolutionists believe that it is possible that the first life assembled itself from nonliving molecules (spontaneous generation). They point to the Miller-Urey experiment, but this

is a blind leap of faith into the dark. Friend Doug Sharp, the one providing the background picture for the cover of this book, uses the following as an example: "Let us suppose that we have a chemical process that assembles proteins at a rate of one million in a nanosecond, using racemic amino acids produced by chance in the Miller-Urey experiment (or off-the-shelf purified ones.) Then we set up a race between this process and a snail that moves one inch in a million years. The snail's job is to move the entire earth, one atom at a time, to the other side of the universe and back, while the chemical process attempts to produce a viable protein for life with four hundred left-handed amino acids in the correct sequence to be useful for life. The snail would win the race."[45]

By way of contrast, Christians believe that the Lord Jesus Christ was and is the source of all life and that He, along with the Father and Holy Spirit, is the Eternal One. He said, "I am ... the Life" (John 14:6, KJV).

Chapter 4

· ·

RECREATIONAL CREATION

This piece of the mosaic is very different from what you have experienced in this book so far, but it is time to smell the roses. Sit back a little and relax in the reverie of God's overwhelming, creative goodness.

Cities are not generally thought of as "God's country," but they should be. Man, the apex of His creation, fills cities. God is more interested in people than animals and flowers. Large cities, like New York and Philadelphia, also have beautiful parks and gardens. New York has its Central Park. Philadelphia's Fairmount Park may be less well known, but it is one of the nation's largest. Our house is one mile from Wissahickon Creek and the trail that runs beside it.

The Wissahickon Trail, part of Fairmount Park, is popular for walkers, bikers, and runners. Horsemen and pet owners use it. Fishermen cast into the creek. Beautiful every season, it is especially lovely in the spring and summer. The first day recounted here was June 1. Professional responsibilities pending for me did not start until the afternoon. Cranking up my aging body for exercising in the morning,

I cycled one mile to the creek, locked the bike under a huge tulip tree, and started my mile, warm-up walk.

When you meet people in this Narnian-like valley, sometimes you wave or say hi. A tall African American man was approaching me on this particular morning, and I waved or said something. He responded with "Praise the Lord." What a refreshing response! I do not remember being greeted that way before on that path. It was special. An unknown brother was encouraging me in the Lord, and remarkable providences followed.

These providences were not thunderous or miraculous, but the verbal prelude of my brother gave them special adornment. He helped me to prize what I was about to see. I also started praying for that unknown friend. I wanted the Lord to encourage his heart as he had encouraged mine. An opportunity had come and gone. My "mentor" seized it for the Lord's glory. At least I could try to seize the next one by praying for him.

When I got to the half-mile marker (where I stretch), I noticed a cluster of butterflies in the distance—warming themselves in a patch of sunlight just above a moist spot on the ground. They were large, yellow, and beautiful—tiger swallowtails.

Evidence of God's handiwork is everywhere along the trail—flitting cardinals, clutches of crows, a feeding falcon, mallard ducks protesting an intrusion, gliding herons, trout in the hands of fishermen, people in horse-drawn carriages, deer running through the woods, daddy-long-legs, attractive damselflies with wings twinkling in flight, rambling rodents, and faint evidence that a skunk had been near. The ferns and foliage are also lovely. Sounds of birds, chipmunks, and a babbling brook fill the air. I had seen many smaller butterflies fluttering quietly hither and yon—sometimes in swirling pairs, but this group had a dignity hard to

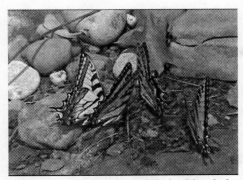

These PA tiger swallowtails had landed, 2005

describe—like slow-motion yellow-caps, dancing in air.

A former track-man, I sometimes pretend that I am still in competition with others I meet on the trail. Sometimes I get to run with horses and win;[46] other times, I "race" humans. On this particular morning, I was privileged to run with tiger swallowtails.

They did not ask permission. At first, an unknown butterfly and I "ran" abreast of each other for perhaps three or four strides. In my heart, I praised the Lord for the privilege of "competing" with one of His delicate creatures—3D poetry in motion. Almost immediately, as the Lord's gracious providences continued to unfold before me, another (or maybe the same), joined the "race" for a longer period. Was this just coincidence?

A refreshing breeze will come and cool our skin, and we thank the Lord of Creation. Soon thereafter another breeze comes—as if in response to our prayer. We wonder, "Is the Lord so tender that He designs breezes specifically to let us know that He hears our hearts and cares?" He does work in mysterious ways. The disciples asked, "What manner of man is this, that even the wind and the sea obey Him?" (Mark 4:41).

I do not know why that second butterfly joined me on the trail, but I do know that the Lord keeps my heart ticking, gives me strength to keep moving, and sends butterflies to delight the hearts of men.

71

Many Americans are oppressed by the idol of science. The media bombard them with messages that science is all-knowing and all-encompassing, but science simply means knowledge and of itself knows nothing. People pool efforts and have achieved impressive results, but no computer ever made by men is as brilliantly colored, as light, and as wonderfully animated as a yellow butterfly dancing along the Wissahickon. (Thank you, remembered brother, if you ever get to read this, for your words of encouragement: "Praise the Lord.")

After doing my mile-walk and mile-run, while stretching, I noticed a thin strip reflecting iridescent beauty caused by some unknown spider. What strength was in that fragile thread? Again, no scientist today could put together such delicate durability.

Returning to my bike, I pedaled up the long path, out of the valley, to home. I was still conscious of the three-word sermon, and continued to be particularly sensitive to God's creative gifts.

As I passed an old cemetery, an attractive mockingbird gently glided before my eyes. These almost constant reminders of God's goodness and presence are so often taken for granted, but even sparrows prance with joy.

When I got back home, my beloved wife asked how things had gone. I told her that I had been running with butterflies.[47]

Running with Birds?

It was a few weeks later that I had the privilege of running with a bird, but this blessing had a darker side. A delicate catbird landed some distance in front of me. As I approached and got close, it would flit further along the trail in front of me. This was not a parallel race, as with

Here the author runs with his daughter (and her daughter)
along the Wissahickon.

the butterfly, but a follow-the-leader one; the catbird was
the leader. It did its land-wait-then-advance thing several
times. It seemed to be teasing me along. Eventually, it had
had enough and flew off to the side.

There are two painful aspects to this story. The first has
to do with the adjective I used to describe this catbird—delicate. Why would I choose such a word?

Some time ago I was driving down a quiet road when
another catbird swooped down in front of my car. I probably
did not know at the time that it was a catbird, but looking
through my rear-view mirror, I saw the pitiful sight of the
bird fluttering on the road. I turned the car around, parked,
and witnessed tragic beauty. Delicate is a good adjective
to use for catbirds, and not just because of their external
beauty. I also saw the fragile, inner-workings of a dying bird

that just minutes before had energized its life. I shed no outward tear, but my heart was aching. Though the sun was shining, it was a dark moment. A bird was dead at the feet of an executioner. Sorrowfully I moved the bird over to the side of the road under a bush. What precious things—birds and butterflies!

The other dark aspect was revealed by the teasing catbird along the Wissahickon. I am no expert on avian husbandry, but I suspect that this bird was protecting its nest. The behavior itself is commendable,[48] but it also points to something dark—disharmony in nature.

Darwin tried to deny the ugliness of nature's struggle for existence by intimating that higher forms of life follow as a consequence,[49] but this is a delusion. Nature's disharmony has nothing to do with producing higher creatures[50] but everything to do with death and extinction.

The reality is that our first parents rebelled against our Maker and brought us into this depraved condition. Why then should any brother preach, "Praise the Lord!"? Because He, the Lord of Creation, promised to reverse and even improve the creation that had fallen.

Sometimes we do not realize the preciousness of a daughter or son until we almost lose one of them, and believers can rejoice, knowing that this disharmonious and preciously delicate creation will one day be renewed and brought into glorious harmony. The wolf will lie down with the lamb, and sorrow and death will flee away (Isa. 11:6-9 and Rev. 21:4-5).

The Lord floods our lives even now with many happy moments, like running with birds and butterflies. Sometimes He puts His grace into verbal form, like when a brother on a path unexpectedly utters words to point us heavenward. He also has a Book out that says, "Let every thing that hath breath praise the Lord. Praise ye the Lord" (Ps. 150:6, KJV).

Chapter 5

. . . .

UP CLOSE AND PERSONAL
WITH CREATOR CHRIST

This chapter is something like the previous one but gets even closer to Creator Christ. If the previous tile was colored pink, then this one may be colored red.

We had just returned from hiking near Moosehead Lake, Maine, when my doctor told me that I was in a potentially life threatening situation. Phlebitis in my leg had not previously been a problem for me, but the long trip back from Maine (seven hours driving on the first day, six on the second) with insufficient pit-stops were major factors in my getting this complication. A deep vein clot developed in my right calf. I tried to exercise the clot out upon return for ten days but eventually decided to see the doctor. The ultrasound Doppler indicated a DVT (deep vein thrombus). I expressed concern that this was a busy time, but the doctor said (and I repeat) that this was potentially life threatening.

Heparin was the medicine prescribed upon my entering Chestnut Hill Hospital in Philadelphia, but additional pain developed in my left lung on a Saturday and became more demanding on Sunday morning. A lung scan revealed that the clot (thrombus) from my leg had moved to my lung; it had become a pulmonary embolus. The left lung, involving an estimated 25-33 percent of the upper lobe, had received the brunt of impact.

Among the options was streptokinase therapy. My wife and I prayed for wisdom and decided to go along with this, which would involve a thirty-six hour infusion of the drug by IV (intravenous). It began around 10 p.m. on Sunday evening. I had been scheduled to speak in Ocean City, New Jersey on that day, teaching God's Word to others, but it seemed, however, that Creator Christ had something different in store. I was to be on the receiving end of learning.

The first ten or twelve minutes of the procedure were fine, but for the next fifteen minutes the pain in my left lung became excruciating. Every muscle in my body that could seemed to respond in sympathy. I had experienced coronary pain some years prior, but this lung pain was much more intense. It was as if a three inch wide sword blade had been jabbed into my left lung through the rib cage and held in place. Writhing in pain, I wondered, *Will this continue for thirty-six hours?*

Squinting my eyes, I thought of Creator Christ who had been crucified long before. I knew He understood exactly what I was going through. I was having a little taste of what He had endured on a cross, but I could not take it. I asked Him in silent prayer then and there to help, and He graciously responded. Jesus had promised never to leave or forsake His own, and I experienced the truth of those words. One of His other creatures was there sympathizing with me in that Intensive Care Unit. She gave me two Tylenol. The pain gradually subsided so that I did not even need Tylenol for the rest of the night.

This was grace from the Creator to me personally. I did not deserve such love, but he gave it anyway. Jesus was there and faithful. Since all healing comes ultimately from the hands of the Creator, He also is the One who restored my lung from all pain. I am breathing normally, and my leg is restored. The Lord Jesus was and is my Healer and Sustainer. My lungs are still healthy. Appreciation can be given to others who assist Him, but He ultimately is worthy of praise.

Lump-in-Throat Intimacy

Of course, there have been many interactions with Creator Christ over the years. My wife's recovery from leukemia is one—answered prayer concerning her health when I thought possibly the next day might bring word of her continued decline or even death—answered prayer also for my mother who experienced open heart (aortic valve) replacement surgery at age ninety-four and was also at the point of death but lived on earth to see her ninety-eighth birthday. The "lump in throat intimacy," however, came with the announcement my son's deliverance during the summer of 2004.

Peter's brain AVM (arteriovenous malformation), according to Dr. Sutton of Children's Hospital, was apparently completely obliterated by Dr. Hurst (of the Hospital of the University of Pennsylvania). This meant that phase two of Peter's planned surgeries was postponed indefinitely. The news forced Dr. Sutton himself to do additional research on what to do when AVMs get completely plugged. Apparently, AVMs are obliterated only about 5-10 percent of the time. He said that he had never seen it before himself. He cautioned that we cannot declare victory yet. Peter should have another arteriogram done again in six weeks to make sure things are still clear.[51] If clear, then another could be done in a year. If that is clear, then "We may be done with this," he said.

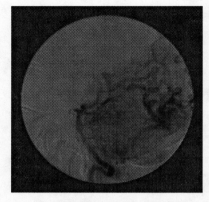

He concluded that there was no proof that additional surgery was needed. There certainly was no reason to go in and mess with Peter's vision, which was checked by a vision specialist and determined to be good. Any negative effect of the surgery apparently was so minimal that it was not detected.

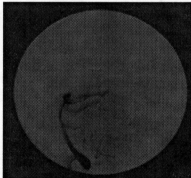

During the revealing session with Dr. Sutton, I was emotionally affected. How good God was to us in answering our prayers beyond our expectations. I told Dr. Sutton, probably with quivering voice, that I had mentioned to Dr. Hurst before the surgical procedure on Peter that many people had been praying for him as well as for Peter. I do not

Notice that the AVM in the first image has disappeared in the second

remember Dr. Hurst's reaction, but Dr. Sutton's commented that Dr. Hurst deserves some credit too. I agreed with him, adding immediately that Dr. Hurst was one of God's gifts too. I also thanked Dr. Sutton for his previous surgery on Peter, adding that he, too, was one of God's gifts.

What Proofs do I Have that People Were Praying?

One person wrote to my cousin, "Thank you for sharing your prayer request for Peter and his family. I will pray and have forwarded the request to many including Max Lucado, a close family friend of our daughter-in-law's family in Texas."

Another wrote, "I'll make it a point to be on my knees around that time." The next day, someone wrote, "Praise God, Paul. I was praying all morning." Yet a fourth person wrote, "This morning at breakfast we said a special prayer for Peter, you and the family, and the doctors, etc. We have been in prayer for him for some time but especially today." A fifth wrote, "We've not stopped (and will continue) to hold you and your family in our hearts and before the throne of grace."

Rarely do I get through on the telephone to my son Paul in Africa, but I called him and got through on the first try. I wanted to pass the good news on to him, too.

My son, Peter, at age nineteen, had been baptized a little more than a week prior and was asked at that time if he had a verse of Scripture to share before being immersed. He quoted from Matthew 28:20: "And, lo, I am with you always, even to the end of the age." Just as the Lord had been with me during my difficult procedure (above), He was also with Peter and the surgeon.

What Place Does this Chapter Have in a Book Like This?

The evolutionary secularist will makes comments like "Time heals all wounds" or "Isn't Mother Nature wonderful," but these implicitly deny credit to Creator Christ. Jesus created time, which of itself can heal nothing, and Mother

Nature is a nonentity. Doctors who do surgery depend on Jesus for their every breath and heart beat, whether or not they realize it. Any mosaic on creation vs. evolution (see Statement of Purpose) should point people in the direction of the Creator. The picture that should come up, being greater than the sum of tile parts, is the Lord Jesus Christ.

Chapter 6

. . . .

DO CREATIONISTS BELIEVE THE EARTH IS FLAT?

Some years ago, the *Philadelphia Daily News* published a cartoon characterizing Christians who hold to the fundamentals of the Bible as out of touch with reality. As an educator, I found it offensive. Sammy, standing on the Bible in a classroom with his back to the others, was looking at a flat "globe" of the earth. The other students and teacher, with quizzical looks on their faces, encompassed a normal (i.e. spherical) globe. The teacher, presumably responding to a student's question, is depicted as saying, "Because Sammy's mom is a fundamentalist, that's why."[52]

The intent seemed to be to ridicule Bible-believing Christians and their view of science. Apparently neither the cartoonist nor the editors realized that Christopher Columbus, a round-earth activist of the highest degree, was driven far more by the Bible than by the science of his day. A dedicated student of the Scriptures, he put his faith into action.

After almost five hundred years, *Libro de las Profecias (Book of Prophecies)*, written and compiled by Columbus, may be seriously considered in English. In her *Christopher*

Columbus--His Life and Discovery in the Light of His Prophecies,[53] Kay Brigham has provided translations of major portions and analysis of his book. She describes it as "a compilation of passages from the Bible which the Admiral believed were pertinent to his mission of discovery, selected by Columbus himself with the help of his friend, Fray Gaspar de Gorricio." Excerpting from folios four through six (using her book as source), I quote Columbus, who in turn was addressing his Spanish sovereigns:

> At this time I have seen and put in study to look into all the Scriptures, cosmography, histories, chronicles and philosophy and other arts, which our Lord opened to my understanding (I could sense His hand upon me), so that it became clear to me that it was feasible to navigate from here to the Indies; and He unlocked within me the determination to execute the idea. And I came to your Highnesses with this ardor. All those who heard about my enterprise rejected it with laughter, scoffing at me. Neither the sciences which I mentioned above, nor the authoritative citations from them, were of any avail. In only your Highnesses remained faith and constancy. Who doubts that this illumination was from the Holy Spirit? I attest that He (the Spirit), with marvelous rays of light, consoled me through the holy and sacred Scriptures . . . encouraging me to proceed, and, continually, without ceasing for a moment, they inflame me with a sense of great urgency. . . .
>
> I am the worst of sinners. The pity and mercy of our Lord have completely covered me whenever I have called (on Him) for them. I have found the sweetest consolation in casting away all my anxiety, so as to contemplate His marvelous presence.

I have already said that for the execution of the enterprise of the Indies, neither reason, nor mathematics, nor world maps were profitable to me; rather the prophecy of Isaiah was completely fulfilled . . . .

Your Highnesses, remember the Gospel texts and the many promises which our Savior made to us, and how all this has been put to a test: (for example) St. Peter, when he leapt into the sea, walked upon (the water) as long as his faith remained firm. The mountains will obey anyone who has faith the size of a kernel of Indian corn. All that is requested by anyone who has faith will be granted. Knock and it will be opened to you. No one should be afraid to take on any enterprise in the name of our Savior, if it is right and if the purpose is purely for His holy service.... The working out of all things was entrusted by our Lord to each person, (but it happens) in conformity with His sovereign will, even though he gives advice to many. He lacks nothing that it may be in the power of men to give him. O, how good is the Lord who wishes people to perform that for which he holds himself responsible! Day and night, and at every moment, everyone should give Him their most devoted thanks.

Noted author, Simon Wiesenthal, in his *Sails of Hope*, confirmed earlier what is now clear from Columbus' own writings: "That religious elements played a great part in Columbus's thoughts and actions is evident from all his writings. It may come as something of a surprise to us that his concept of sailing west to reach the Indies was less the result of geographical theories than of his faith in certain Biblical texts, specifically the Book of Isaiah."[54]

Some Today Despise Columbus.

William Loren Katz, though affirming Columbus' "enormous skills, courage and ambition," added that "Columbus carried in his heart the burning embers of hate" and repaid the "generosity" of the natives with "treachery."[55] Others have similar concerns.

Sadly, exploitation of peoples and lands followed in Columbus' wake, and Columbus himself contributed in part. His own testimony of being "the worst of sinners" has already been mentioned, but he also viewed himself as "Servant ... of the Most High Savior, Christ the Son of Mary."[56] He trusted apparently in Creator Jesus who forgives the sins of repentant sinners. Indeed, he named the very first island he landed on San Salvador out of regard for his "Holy Savior" (translation).

The esteemed Harvard historian, Samuel Eliot Morison, who dedicated a copy of his Pulitzer Prize-winning book, *Admiral of the Ocean Sea* to his shipmate, Lieutenant Commander Millard J. Klein, Kay Brigham's father, was more generous in his appraisal of Admiral Columbus. He wrote, "I cannot forget the eternal faith that sent this man forth, to the benefit of all future ages."[57] Columbus sought the conversion of the natives. On the premise that people are lost without Christ, such a concern could be interpreted as an expression of genuine love rather than of hate. He prayed on San Salvador, "O Lord Almighty and Everlasting God, by Thy holy Word Thou hast created the heaven, and the earth, and the sea; blessed and glorified be Thy Name, and praised be Thy Majesty, which hath deigned to use us, Thy humble servants, that Thy holy Name may be proclaimed in this second part of the earth."[58]

According to Morison, Columbus and his family were different from many of the others who wanted "to get gold quick and go home." Only Columbus, "his family and a few faithful, humble souls" cared for establishing a "permanent settlement" and the transfer of Christianity to the Indies.

Morison was not unaware of some of Columbus' shortcomings, but he also wrote of his humanity: "It was to Columbus' credit that humanity prevailed over glory. It must have been a temptation to parade this brilliant savage royalty with their gold and feather ornaments at court. But he thought of the cold weather in which they would suffer and die, of what the pretty daughters might expect from his seamen, of the disillusion that would await these innocent souls in Castile. So he took compassion on them, declined the cacique's request, and sent the Indians ashore in the ship's boat after receiving their homage and fealty."

Kay Brigham's assessment of Columbus is very positive: "On account of faith—'being sure of what we hope for and certain of what we do not see' (Heb. 11:1), Columbus discovered America, the most significant event for the human race after the birth, death, and resurrection of the Savior of the world. Faith liberated Columbus from the chains of human myopia, launching him on a divine mission and propelling him to a providential destination ... initiating the histories of the United States, Canada, and the numerous American republics and the phenomenal expansion of the Christian faith."

Columbus and the Bible

Scriptural passages cited by Columbus in his book, *Libro de las Profecias (Book of Prophecies)* include the following:

The LORD reigneth, let the earth rejoice; let the multitude of isles be glad thereof (Ps. 97:1 KJV).

Sing unto the LORD a new song, and His praise from the ends of the earth, ye that go down to the sea, and all that is therein; the isles, and the inhabitants thereof (Isa. 42:10 KJV).

Listen, O isles, unto Me; and hearken, ye people from far (Isa. 49:1 KJV).

My righteousness is near; My salvation is gone forth.... The isles shall wait upon Me, and on Mine arm shall they trust (Isa. 51:5 KJV).

I am sought of them that asked not for Me; I am found of them that sought Me not; I said, Behold Me, behold Me, unto a nation that was not called by My name (Isa. 65:1 KJV).

Go ye therefore, and teach all nations, baptizing them in the name of the Father and of the Son and of the Holy Ghost: Teaching them to observe all things whatsoever I have commanded you: And, lo, I am with you always, even unto the end of the world (Matt. 28:19-20 KJV).

But ye shall receive power after that the Holy Ghost is come upon you; and you shall be witnesses unto me both in Jerusalem, and in all Judea, and in Samaria, and unto the uttermost part of the earth (Acts 1:8 KJV).

"Columbus always loved to apply the Sacred Scriptures to his own life and adventures," according to Morison. Wilbur E. Garret, *National Geographic* editor, shares that this was also true at his death: "Son Ferdinand reports that Columbus repeated the words attributed to Christ on the cross—'Into your hands, Father, I commend my soul'—and died."[59]

But, We Might Ask, "Does the Bible Really Teach that the Earth is a Sphere?"

Recall the cartoon mentioned at the beginning of the chapter. Did the Holy Spirit, in moving men to write Scripture, want to instruct us specifically about earth's sphericity? In answering this question, it is important to say that the Bible's primary purpose is to record God's redemptive act in Creator Christ. As people in deep trouble, we need to learn that God became flesh to accomplish salvation for us on the cross. Information about the earth's shape, therefore, is not as critical for us as learning about the solution to our problems of sin and death. We need radical heart surgery. Deuteronomy 29:29 reads as follows, "The secret things belong to the LORD our God, but the things revealed belong to us and to our children forever, that we may follow all the words of this law."

The Prophet Isaiah, nevertheless, did report, that our Lord "sits enthroned above the circle of the earth, and its people are like grasshoppers" (Isa. 40:22). This does not clash with the notion that the earth is round (a sphere), but our Lord's sovereignty over all was and is the primary focus of the passage.

Elsewhere, Job said that our Lord "spreads out the northern [skies] over empty space; he suspends the earth over nothing" (26:7). Perhaps Job, seeing the sun and moon suspended in space, was affirming something similar for the earth. In the same book, our Lord Himself said, "The earth takes shape like clay under a seal; its features stand out like those of a garment" (Job 38:14). Is this a reference to the earth's rotation?

My earthly father used Acts 1:8 to support the concept of earth's sphericity. It reads as follows: "But you will receive power when the Holy Spirit comes on you; and you will be my witnesses in Jerusalem, and in all Judea and Samaria, and to the ends of the earth" (NIV). The Authorized Version translates "ends" with a singular, "to the uttermost part of the earth." A sphere would have one uttermost part (at the point of intersection of a diameter going from any point on the earth through the center and intersecting the sphere in exactly one point at the opposite end. The original language of this passage (Greek) supports the singular translation.

Additionally, the Lord Jesus stressed the importance of every scriptural jot and tittle (Matt. 5:18). When God said, "I am the God of Abraham, the God of Isaac, and the God of Jacob" (Matt. 22:32), His point seems to hang on the present tense of the verb, to be ("am"). Buried patriarchs were alive, in other words—in their spirits, when God spoke the words cited above to Moses, who lived hundreds of years *after* the patriarchs had physically died. If our Lord placed such weight on verb tense, should not we follow His example by distinguishing between singular and plural forms?

Chapter 7

An Open Door for Creation to Be Taught in Public Schools

J esus said of the Philadelphia Church that He had put before them an "open door which no one can shut" (Rev. 3:8). Though originally a different Philadelphia was in view, it is interesting that for the last three years, Christian released time (CRT) Philadelphia[60] has been entering through new doors, and public school children are learning about creation and the God of creation.

We have already seen how Christians can experience victory through prayer (chapter five) and how Columbus experienced a victory through faith in God's Word (chapter six). In this chapter, we learn that CRT Philadelphia has required both prayer and faith. With parental approval, classes meet off campus during regular school hours. *The Philadelphia Inquirer*[61] featured our efforts, and mention was also made in *WORLD* Magazine.[62] Eleven public schools in or near Philadelphia were involved in the 2004-2005 school year, and CRT is legal in every state. Not only have public school children been hearing about creation and Creator Christ, but the Gospel of salvation has been taught, too!

This is a picture of public school children in Philadelphia
answering questions asked during a CRT class.

At this point, I want to become anecdotal. The victory I
share below happened near the beginning of our efforts to
establish CRT in Philadelphia. As Nehemiah encountered
opposition, so did we. If God's people can take courage that
God helped in centuries past, perhaps they can also take
courage from more recent efforts to overcome opposition.

It was on a Monday. I wrote, "This may be the best day
yet for CRT Philadelphia!" Following a meeting with the
superintendent of Philadelphia's school district, a sister in
the Lord, who had served in the District for thirty-six years,
prayed out loud as we walked to my car. She was exhilarated
and thanked the Lord for, as she put it, shutting "the lion's
mouth." She was *not* referring to the superintendent, who
actually had been very gracious toward us.

As we were driving home, she said that a song was in her heart, and we both started to sing: "What a mighty God we serve! What a mighty God we serve! Angels bow before Him; heaven and earth adore Him! What a mighty God we serve!"

Here is what happened that gave us a sense of victory. We had arrived at the superintendent's office just after noon and were waiting in the outside office, looking over yearbooks from different schools in the city. A man walked into the same office a few minutes after we arrived and told the secretary that he was to meet with the Superintendent in a few minutes. I surmised he might be the lawyer with whom we had been having difficulty.

Let us jump back in time by a few months to provide context. This was the lawyer who had informed a principal by e-mail that our CRT class could not begin on the day we had, in agreement with parents and principal, set for it to begin. It was a critical moment. One student had already arrived at the school office anticipating the commencement of classes. The principal was in the office with me and my coworker (the very same one who was singing with me months later on the way home). The administrator was perplexed. What should she do? Certainly she did not want to get fired for disobeying the school district's lawyer. I asked her if I could use her phone to call that lawyer. The outcome was that we were able to start CRT classes that day, but it was not without a struggle.

Returning now to our encounter with this lawyer outside the superintendent's office, I called across to him asking if he was who I thought he might be. I stood up and extended a hand, introducing myself and my coworker. He made a comment something like, "It's nice to put a face on a name."

A few minutes later, the superintendent came to the door and invited us all in. His office was busy with paperwork, so he decided to use an adjacent conference room. I noted that he was wearing an educational tie. I had seen another one on the front cover of the *Inquirer Magazine* (where he had been featured) and decided to ask how many educational ties he had. He said he had about fifty–some being pretty worn. The one he was wearing was new looking.

He then turned the first part of the meeting over to me, since I had complained about actions from the lawyer present. I gave a copy of my prepared letter/document to the superintendent and also to the lawyer (sliding it across the table to him). I commented that one advantage of having something in writing is that one can see as well as hear the concerns. (I did not make it explicit, but I had in mind the lawyer's disrespectful wording he had written using a red font and which eventually found its way into e-mail boxes of about forty-five principals.) I then proceeded to read what I had prepared. The document pointed out how the lawyer had actually discouraged Christian released time in Philadelphia, something the federal government said should not be done. Discouraging released time, in other words, is not being neutral.

I heard the superintendent flipping through the three and one-half pages. When I got about halfway through reading aloud, the superintendent said that he was a fast reader and had read through the document. He added that he was willing to send out word to all the Philadelphia school parents the availability of religious released time. I did not fully grasp his intent at first, so I queried about the damage that had already been done by the lawyer's communication. I was also concerned that Skilton House Ministries' efforts to communicate nuts and bolts information to particular parents regarding a specific released time opportunity might be frustrated, but my host was apparently saying this concept (communicating nuts-and-bolts specifics) was OK. In fact, he said that he wanted to "push the envelope" to encourage faith-based initiatives.

The superintendent then stepped out momentarily to contact an associate of his, the Assistant Director of School and Community Relations. He wanted him to participate in the meeting. (I had previously met this man and had also conversed with him over the phone.) When the superintendent was out, I asked the lawyer who was still present where it says in writing that schools may not send brochures home about released time. His response was that it was part of the Constitution. (I did not respond that passing out brochures–thus informing parents of a released time opportunity–was not the establishment of religion; nor did I suggest that he himself should not be "prohibiting the free exercise" of the same.) The lawyer did say that he and I had a different interpretation of the law.

The superintendent returned, and eventually his associate. He directed him to facilitate a near-the-end-of-school-year communication to be sent out to all the parents informing them of various opportunities–including religious released time. I sensed that the superintendent wanted to be supportive of what Skilton House was doing. He even suggested that churches perhaps could help with extended hours. In this concept, students could leave an hour early (for released time instruction) and maybe beyond that for character development and moral training.

I asked explicitly about brochures that Skilton House prepared for parents to be sent home via homerooms–fliers that gave specific times for specific locations, etc. He did not seem to have a problem with this–even mentioning the church name would be OK. He encouraged me to send samples of what we had done in the past to his associate who, in turn, could run it by both the superintendent and the lawyer. Basically, the superintendent seemed to be open to the position I was advocating. He tipped his hat to the lawyer by saying that it should be legal, but he seemed open to giving the law considerable latitude (as opposed to a very narrow interpretation).

Near the end, I passed a copy of a recent Skilton House newsletter to the superintendent. He seemed pleased that the Marshall School (featured on the front) was involved. I also showed him a picture of Christian released time happening at the Levering School.

In summary, the superintendent indicated that he wanted to encourage faith-based initiatives. He referred to "Ten Commandment" book covers he had made available to students in Chicago. I told him that Skilton House would be willing to help him with such a project in Philadelphia. He seemed pleased and receptive to the suggestion, and we have since facilitated such. We ended very cordially, shaking hands, etc. The lawyer was still across the table; I waved a good-bye to him.

The superintendent's associate walked with my coworker and me as we left, going down the elevator and even out to the sidewalk. It was a delightful day in many ways. He wanted me to put some paragraphs together and send to him for his adjusting. I reminded him that there were two things that needed to be done. In addition to preparing something for all the parents in Philadelphia, we needed to encourage the principals who already were hurting due to the lawyer's previous communication. He agreed, and I was to send him both pieces of information.

I really got a kick out of my coworker's comment as we walked away to the car—something like: "The Lord shut the lion's mouth!" She was referring, of course, to Daniel's experience in the lion's den. Daniel was unharmed by the lions because the Lord had shut their mouths.

Much work still had to be done. What area is there for the reader? May we all get out of the stands and onto the playing fields for the Lord. He has won the battle, but there is still much cleanup to do for Him. Bruised lives are all over the field. Satan has left a mess, but this is the victory that overcomes the world—even our faith. Believing in creation and the Creator involves walking by faith. Some people think that public school children cannot learn about creation during regular school hours, but they can! Let the enemy wince from our salt. Let the light of the Lord shine deep into the hearts of public school children.

Practical Steps to Advance Creation and Christian Released Time

The Creator is creative. As image bearers, let us be creative. Not long ago, I sent out an offer to various CRT workers, principals, and administrators, asking, "Would you like a free subscription to the beautiful *Creation* magazine? All you have to do is send me the name and address you want me to use." Here is a response I received from one principal: "Hi Paul. Thank you for the gift subscription. My home address is .... Merry Christmas to you and prayers for continued blessings this New Year. Your friend ...."

We can be practical in other ways. With help from brothers and sisters in Christ, you and I both can at least try to start up a Christian released time effort for public school children near you! Here are some steps:

First, be in love with the Lord Jesus yourself. Realize that He is far more than just a great religious leader. He is the Creator of the entire universe! If you do not have an intimate, loving relationship with Him, then you must get right with Him. Pray: "Jesus, I am unworthy of Your love. I have done many things that displease You. Please forgive

95

me. Let Your blood cover over all my sins, and bring me into Your heaven when the time comes. Thank you. I love You. In Your precious Name, Amen."

Second, pray for your project. Humans can be proud, but the Lord wants them humble. He wants you dependent on Him. People know from the Bible that He wants them sharing their faith, but He wants them doing so in His strength. He does not want them forgetting Him. Bathe your efforts in prayer; seek His blessing. Ask Him to establish the work of your hands.

Third, discern a school close to your home (or church building). Write down its name. Get the name of the principal. Envision the kids you see running around at recess getting to know you personally in a CRT class. They may be foreigners to you now, but you want to get to know them for Jesus.

Fourth, walk around the school in ever widening circles until you come up with some idea for a location in which to conduct classes. It might be a church building or a community building of some kind. Most frequently, a church building will be located not too far away. It does not have to be the one you attend. Discover, like Sherlock, who the pastor or leader is responsible for that building. Get names, address, phone numbers, and maybe even an e-mail address. After working with us for three years, here is what one pastor wrote who wants to continue as we were contemplating year four: "Thank you for the information. I wish to stay involved with released time and do more partnering with Levering School. Bob"

Fifth, you may contact me (humber@juno.com). What you need to do at this point is to set up a meeting with the pastor or community leader. Pray that the Lord might open the eyes of this person to catch the vision of reaching public school children for Jesus.

Sixth, meet with that pastor/leader. I can provide you with documentation that this is legal and that it has been happening in other parts of the country. Discuss with the pastor times he might be able to meet with the principal. Encourage him to be thinking about people in his church who might be able to help as walkers, listeners, and even teachers.

Seventh, you can call the principal and say something like this: "Thank you for answering my call. I have met with Pastor X, who pastors Y Church near your school. We would like to meet with you to discuss implementation of released time for religious instruction. If you do not know much about it, then we can help you have a better understanding. If you already know about it, then we can help you see how it is being applied in other parts of our country." Try to secure a specific time, location, and date—consistent with the information you have already received from the pastor/leader.

Eighth, with my e-mail assistance, we can prepare a draft brochure so that when the meeting time arrives, you will have something to show him/her. Principals like to see exactly how the implementation will work. It can be stated in the brochure that the times and days are only tentative but that you wanted to display some provisional ideas on how it all this can work together.

Ninth, after times and dates have been agreed upon for CRT to begin at the school, then there is a need to secure parental approval. There are several ways to do this. One of the most effective ways is to distribute fliers to children after school, on their way home. The School District of Philadelphia (SDP) has Policy #117.0 which states that it is OK to distribute fliers on school sidewalks, and it is likely OK for your school, too. SDP Policy 117.0 reads in part: "The sidewalks, walkways and streets around a school or school facility are deemed in most circumstances to be public forums on which citizens are entitled to engage in constitutionally protected forms of expression. These protected forms of expression include the right to: (a) hand out leaflets, circulars, papers, books, etc.; (b) solicit signatures on petitions; (c) picket or parade, including the use of posters and banners." It continues: "Pamphlets or other printed materials may contain statements that anger or excite the reader or which are critical of the school or its administration." If kids are enthusiastic, then parents are motivated to sign for release. I can help prepare this "kids-friendly" brochure. You would run off perhaps two hundred or more copies for distribution.

Tenth, you, with the help of others, may plan to distribute the fliers about a week or so before the first class (perhaps locating yourselves at different exit doors). To make your distribution effort more interesting, you can have a card table set up near you for free Ten Commandment book covers. (Ask me to mail one hundred copies free of charge from my supply.)

Eleventh, develop friendly relationships with the principal, secretaries, and other staff. When we first began, we did encounter resistance from a school district lawyer (referred to above), but this has improved. Lawyers in Philadelphia now know that what we are doing is legal. This does not mean that there will be no resistance from principals. Some are very friendly and cooperative, but others are not as friendly. This underscores the importance of prayer. Pray that the principals might be friendly and cooperative.

Twelfth, it is important to develop a growing list of approved students (students with parent-permission slips signed). It is good for you to have two copies of this constantly updated list handy for each session. You keep a personal copy, but you want to be able to submit an attendance report following the class (either when you return the kids to school for dismissal or the next day). You can use the master list to facilitate taking attendance. It is also good for the principal to have an official (updated) list so that teachers can be alerted as to which students have been approved for release.

Thirteenth, be aware that children are responsible to make up work missed, but according to a research study, released time actually improves academic performance and builds a foundation for positive character development. Barry Krisberg, President of the National Council on Crime and Delinquency, said, "An increasing number of studies are showing that religion has a positive impact on the behavior of students. In this study, it was interesting to find that academic performance was also significantly better than students who did not participate in the program."[63]

Fourteenth, ethnicity is an important consideration. Since public school children in Philadelphia are mixed ethnically, it is wise to have mixed support teams (those who will be with the children). Here is one area where Christians of different people groups need to come together, demonstrating Christian unity. I have a lesson called, "One Human Race" and am happy to share it by e-mail. Children sometimes will ask, "Why are there different kinds of people?" This is a good question, and it is good to have the answer (cf. 2 Peter 3:15).

Fifteenth, having two people who are able to teach is wise. If one falters, then the other is there to fill in the gap. The teachers also do not have to be great Bible scholars. Children can feel love and sincerity. Be humble and honest. If a student asks a hard question, you can tell him/her that you do not know but that you will try to get the answer for the following meeting.

Sixteenth, as far as lessons are concerned, be creative. I have a variety of lessons that I have used and can share free of charge. There are also other resources available. Being alert to current events is good. To the extent possible, try to be responsive to questions. It is also important for you to have a definite plan in mind should the children not have questions at the beginning.

Seventeenth, children like snacks at the end. Be ready with some refreshments. Also, you need to be prepared to escort the children back to the school. If your class is for the last hour in the school day, make sure you return the children in time for dismissal. (You do not want them to miss a school bus.) Of course, you also need to escort the children to the release time location at the beginning. Make sure ahead of time that the destination building will be open. It is difficult to arrive and find a locked building. I have, on occasion, met with student on outside stairs. It can work. Children like the outdoors, but inside is to be preferred.

Walking with the Lord, serving Him in this way, and promoting creation can be exhilarating. Many of the children know little about Jesus. What a privilege it is to share with them about the greatest Person who ever walked this planet—the Creator of the Universe and the One who saves unworthy people like them and us.

Final Words from a Chief Justice of the US Supreme Court and a Former President

Many people are confused by the so-called "separation of church and State" doctrine—that the two spheres are and should be almost antagonistic towards each other. This is absurd thinking. Imagine an atheist, for example, saying that all laws against murder or stealing should be repealed because both are condemned by the Ten Commandments

100

(a religious document). No, church and state should be in agreement that murder and stealing are wrong.

Here is what former Chief Justice William Rehnquist wrote in 1985, "The 'wall of separation between church and state' is a metaphor based on bad history, a metaphor which has proved useless as a guide to judging. It should be frankly and explicitly abandoned."

I quote another William. I did not vote for him, but I admire and appreciate his following words very much. They pertain to freedoms public school children should enjoy in the classroom. On July 12, 1995, former President William Jefferson Clinton affirmed:

> Nothing in the First Amendment converts our public schools into religion-free zones, or requires all religious expression to be left behind at the schoolhouse door. While the government may not use schools to coerce the consciences of our students, or to convey official endorsement of religion, the public schools also may not discriminate against private religious expression during the school day. Religion is too important in our history and our heritage for us to keep it out of our schools...[I]t shouldn't be demanded, but as long as it is not sponsored by school officials and doesn't interfere with other children's rights, it mustn't be denied.

Chapter 8

. . . .

My Interaction with Oxford's Richard Dawkins

Jumping across the ocean immediately after discussing the implementation of Christian released time in America's public school may seem abrupt and disconnected, but both chapters (tiles) are part of the same mosaic. Dr. Richard Dawkins influences American educators, and his words need to be challenged. This chapter describes an e-mail correspondence I had with this leader of evolution. A primary topic of our correspondence was the February 1986 Oxford Union Debate involving evolutionists and creationists. Dr. Dawkins, who for quite awhile refused to debate creationists, was himself then a participant. The recent exchanges reveal a deception, even affirmed by Dr. Dawkins himself.

Currently a professor at Oxford and the author of many articles and books (including *The Blind Watchmaker*, *River Out of Eden*, and *Climbing Mount Improbable*), Dr. Dawkins and Professor John Maynard-Smith debated Professors A.E. Wilder-Smith and Edgar Andrews at Oxford University on February 14, 1986. If the Scopes Trial of 1925 should receive attention (in current media and even later in this book), then so should this debate. Few, however, have been made aware of it. In fact, there is evidence of a cover-up. In fact, there seems to be little record of this debate ever having happened.

I sent an e-mail to Dr. Dawkins on May 28, 2003 asking if he had memory of it. He responded that he did, adding:[64] "And the date (which of course I do not remember) is attested by the following article by the well-known historian of science Professor John Durant." He provided the weblink.[65]

Also in his reply, Dr. Dawkins added, "Durant also records (which I had forgotten) that Maynard Smith and I won the debate by 198 votes to 15."

As I questioned the accuracy of this tally, I wrote back: "Arthur Ernest Wilder Smith mentions in his 1993 book, *The Time Dimension*, that the Creationists' side received 114 votes out of approximately 300 cast." I asked, "Is it possible that Durant's figure cited above (15) should be 115? The total, 313, would then be much closer to 300 than Durant's 213 total. In other words, do you think there may be a typo in Durant's figures?"

Dr. Dawkins responded, "I have no idea. It is obviously possible. I do recall, however, that there was something fishy about Wilder-Smith's credentials. The 'About the Author' notes on the back of his books claims that he studied natural sciences at Oxford. This aroused my suspicions because Natural Sciences is not a recognized degree course at Oxford (though it is at Cambridge). So I made inquiries and the university offices could find no record that anybody of his name had ever been registered at Oxford. If you are interested (I believe he is now dead) you might do well to investigate the authenticity of the three doctorates that he claimed to possess."

On May 30, 2003, I wrote back: "Thanks for responding, but I seek additional clarification. Previously, you had written, 'Durant also records (which I had forgotten) that Maynard Smith and I won the debate by 198 votes to 15,' but this does not seem to be quite accurate. First, there is no space between 1 and 5 in your quotation of Durant, but there *is* a blank space in Durant's account suggesting all the more the possibility of a typo."

Dr. Dawkins responded to this point with, "Yes, except that Durant does mention 15 twice in his account."

I also wrote in my May 30, 2003, "The original numbers might have been 198 to 1(1)5, as I had previously suggested as a possibility. Second, do you have any memory of a landslide victory (numerically speaking) —even if you did not remember the *exact* numbers?"

The Oxford professor responded, "No, now that I think about it carefully, I do not have a clear memory of a landslide victory. And you are right that I probably would have, if it had been a landslide."

Near the end of my May 30 communication, I wrote, "It's hard to believe that there would be such a minimal accounting of such an interesting event."

To this comment, Dr. Dawkins responded, "Well, I don't actually think it was an interesting event. I think it was rather an absurd event, and I would not now agree to take part in one like it for the reasons given in my published correspondence with Stephen Jay Gould. I was younger and less experienced when I agreed to do that Oxford Union debate. Even then, I remember, I agreed to do it only to support a young student of mine who was one of the other speakers in the debate."

Dr. Dawkins continued, "Wilder-Smith I remember as a genial old buffoon, who had no understanding that Maynard Smith was running rings round him. Edgar Andrews cut an altogether less jovial figure. In his speech he tried to come across as a sophisticated scientist and philosopher, NOT as a Bible-bashing fundamentalist creationist. But I had a copy of one of his books, and during my speech I started to read passages aloud in order to demonstrate that, in spite of his speech, he was really an old-style six-day Genesis, Adam-and-Eve creationist. Naturally that would not appeal to an educated Oxford audience. And Edgar Andrews tried *desperately* hard to stop me reading. He stood up to interrupt me repeatedly, probably four or five times, and tried to persuade the President to stop me reading. She repeatedly refused to stop me and I proceeded to read, whereupon Andrews finally gave up and sat with his head in his hands, looking for all the world like a broken man. Bizarre, when you think that all I was doing was reading whole paragraphs (not out of context, therefore) from his own book."

I followed up with additional inquiries to Dr. Dawkins on May 31, 2003. My persistence apparently upset him. He started to doubt that he was "dealing with somebody sane." He asked, "Are you some kind of obsessive compulsive? I mean, what *is* this obsessive interest in an utterly trivial event which happened fifteen years ago or whenever it was? Just look at what you have written below. Anyone would think you were Sherlock Holmes on the track of a murder!"

He added, "I am not going to waste any more time. This correspondence is at an end. I replied to you originally out of courtesy, but enough is enough. And no, I am not interested in following up Wilder-Smith's history. The man is too unimportant to waste time over."

The reader should be aware, at this point, that Dr. Dawkins did eventually resume communications with me, but, first, exactly what was it that I wrote that upset this Oxford professor? My letter was as follows:

Dear Dr. Dawkins,

Thanks again for responding. In your most recent note, you wrote (regarding the numbers in Durant's report), "Yes, except that Durant does mention fifteen twice in his account." There is a problem with this, also. Neither time in Durant's report, when fifteen is represented numerically, does it look like your representation for "15." Not only is there a space between the two digits both times, but the numeral used for one does not look like your "1" or other numerals for one in Durant's article. You mention (below) having your suspicions aroused about another matter, but I am suspicious that numbers in Durant's report have been tampered with—especially in view of your not remembering such a landslide.

In this communication, I also offered Dr. Dawkins a fellow scholar's opinion of Dr. Wilder-Smith:

One of the most remarkable things I discovered was the testimony of Dr. Dean Kenyon, Professor of Biology, San Francisco State University: 'Dr. A.E. Wilder-Smith was one of the two or three most important scientists in my life. He very powerfully influenced my intellectual development and my change of opinion on the origin of man. His writings, in particular *The Creation of Life* and *The Scientific Alternative to Neo-Darwinian Evolutionary Theory*, and the discussions I had with him were outstanding and had a great impact on my views and thoughts on origins. He was a courageous, supportive and gracious man, and he is greatly missed.' It's difficult to know how to put this together with your representation: "Wilder-Smith I remember as a genial old buffoon...."

The matter of his having studied "natural sciences" at Oxford raised your suspicions, but there does not seem to be a claim that he was working for a degree in Natural

Sciences. Surely Oxford teaches "natural sciences," even if there is no specific degree track for it.

I also pursued the matter of Dr. Dawkins reducing Professor Andrews to "a broken man":

> Finally, referring to Professor Edgar Andrews, you wrote, "But I had a copy of one of his books, and during my speech I started to read passages aloud in order to demonstrate that, in spite of his speech, he was really an old-style 6-day Genesis Adam-and-Eve creationist." This raises three related questions: Had there been a prior agreement *not* to bring religion in the debate? Was what you were reading *religious*? Might Professor Andrews's protestations have been along the line that you were doing what you had agreed before the debate not to do?

Two Apologies from Dr. Dawkins

To Dr. Dawkins' credit, he subsequently wrote two apologies. In the first (May 31, 2003), he said, "I apologise. My last letter was not polite. There is no reason why you shouldn't be interested in Wilder-Smith et al., if that is how you want to spend your time." (Apparently the English spell the word, apologize, differently than Americans.) He added, nevertheless, that he thought some of what I was doing was "trivial."

His second apology was revealing. He wrote, "I should apologise again. You are right that the Durant article looks tampered with. There really is a gap in the middle of the 15, on BOTH occasions where 15 is mentioned. You can verify this by copying it into a word processor such as MS Word. There is definitely a space in the middle. And the 1 is not a 1 at all but an l, as you can verify by telling the word processor to render it in all caps. 15 becomes L 5!"

In the very next paragraph, he added, "I am persuaded that somebody has tampered with Durant's article, and I find it extremely bizarre. It cannot be Durant himself of course, for if he had wanted to give a false figure he would obviously just have typed a false figure. But whoever it was, it is weird to do it so INEPTLY. I mean, why use an L when you could use a proper 1! And why not eliminate the space? It almost looks like a double bluff. Somebody wanted it to LOOK as though it had been tampered with! If I can find John Durant's address (it's awhile since I heard from him and I know he has moved) I'll tell him. He'll be intrigued."

Concerning Professor Andrews, Dr. Dawkins wrote, "No, there DEFINITELY were no prior agreements about what not to bring in, neither religion nor anything else." Secondly, "Yes, of course Andrews's book was about religion. That was my whole POINT! He had been trying, in his speech, to disguise the fact that his real grounds for being a creationist were not scientific at all, but religious. That was why I was reading from his book, and that was why he was trying to stop me. But there were no prior agreements to violate."

On June 1, I wrote:

Dear Dr. Dawkins,

Since reading these words, I was sent an account which I had not seen before, written by Dr. Wilder-Smith. In his book, *The Time Dimension* (pp. 19-23), he reports on the Oxford Union Debate: "Before the debate commenced it was agreed in committee in the Oxford Union's President's office that no religious or non-scientific, non-repeatable material should be introduced into the debate. Only repeatable falsifiable scientific fact would be acceptable. To this point of policy the *representatives of both sides of the House readily and specifically agreed*" (emphasis added). He later continued, "A possible reason for the total cover-up of the Oxford Union debate is, maybe, illuminated by Richard Dawkins' impassioned plea to the audience before the voting took place and after the debate itself was over. Dawkins implored (the word he himself used) the voting public not to give a single vote for the creationist position, for every vote in favor of creationism would, he maintained, be a blot on the escutcheon of the ancient University of Oxford. ... Since it had been agreed not to let religious factors play any role in the proceedings, Professor Andrews brought up the point of order, that no religious considerations should play any role. The president supported Professor Andrews and Richard Dawkins sat down."

Regarding Professor Maynard Smith, Wilder-Smith said that he "then stood up and said he was glad that I had stuck to pure science in the debate, science which was impeccable, but said that I believed in a small tribal God, which was not acceptable today. He and his friends believed that the whole, big universe was God which was a superior belief to mine. Again, I was attacked not on scientific but on purely religious grounds, which was entirely out of order."

Wilder-Smith added: "Subsequent efforts on the part of a librarian employed by the University of Oxford to obtain from the Oxford Union my address and a report on the debate were answered to the effect that it knew of no such debate ever having taken place and could give no information as to my person or even my present address. Thus I was obliged to send to the librarian concerned a photocopy of the invitation which the Oxford Union had sent to my correct address in Switzerland and which has in the meantime never changed, together with their formulation of the title of the motion before the House. The librarian obtained my address from friends in Australia as it was not forthcoming from Oxford."

Perhaps now I can better understand why you are reluctant to debate those who believe that life in all of its brilliance could not have come about by non-intelligent chance. If there is some truth to what Wilder-Smith wrote, you had a challenging experience in 1986 and do not want it repeated. Should you ever change your mind, please let me know. I also would like to know why the debate numbers were changed from 198-115 to 198-15. Do you have John Durant's e-mail address?

On June 2, Dr. Dawkins wrote regarding the agreement in committee idea: "That is pure fantasy. A lie. It never happened. In any case, it would have been absurd to reach such an agreement, since the creationist position *is* a religious position. How could one *possibly* debate it, for or against, without mentioning it? I would never have agreed to such a thing. It would be like agreeing to a debate on pigs and then agreeing not to mention pigs." (Further down in Dawkins' letter, he wrote, "Wilder-Smith's account lies somewhere between fantasy, lies, and paranoid delusion.")

Regarding Dr. Wilder-Smith's statement that there was a cover-up of the debate having actually occurred, Dr. Dawkins wrote: "Cover-up? *What* cover-up? I have agreed that John Durant's figures have been tampered with. But that is nothing to do with the Oxford Union or with Oxford University. That is not a cover-up; that is a dishonest individual, some kind of hacker perhaps, with access to a particular non-official web-site."

Regarding the matter of an impassioned plea to the audience, Dawkins wrote: "I may well have said something of the kind, in the course of my speech. It is the sort of thing one does say when asking people to vote in a debate. I do think every single vote in favour of creationism would be a disgrace to Oxford, or indeed to any university. I say so frequently and I shall continue to do so."

As to Dr. Wilder-Smith's statement that "Professor Andrews brought up the point of order, that no religious considerations should play any role," Dawkins responded: "If this is a reference to Andrews's pathetic and undignified attempts to stop me reading from his own book, it was *me* the president supported, and *Andrews* who sat down (eventually, after several attempts to stop me speaking). I told you that before. My memory is extremely clear on the matter. I do not remember what he actually said when trying to get the President to stop me, but I remember very clearly that it was he who eventually sat down (with his head in his hands)."

(I would like to interject an editorial comment here. Dr. Wilder-Smith's book was written about six years after the event. Dr. Dawkins, who initially reported the debate result as 198 to 15, eventually affirmed that he did not remember such a landslide. If his memory was so fuzzy about the debate outcome, how can one be sure of his "extremely clear" memory of a lesser aspect? He was writing not six years after—but seventeen years after the event!)

In response to Dr. Wilder-Smith's recollection of Professor Maynard Smith's words ("Regarding Professor Maynard Smith, Wilder-Smith said that he 'then stood up and said he was glad that I had stuck to pure science in the debate, science which was impeccable, but said that I believed in a small tribal God, which was not acceptable today'"), Dawkins wrote, "I don't remember, but it is plausible that Maynard Smith might have said something like this in passing, before getting on to the main part of his speech. It is not an 'attack' but a highly justified point. I would gladly make it myself, any time."

In response to Wilder-Smith's statement, "He and his friends believed that the whole, big universe was God which was a superior belief to mine. Again, I was attacked not on scientific but on purely religious grounds, which was entirely out of order," Dawkins wrote, "I do not remember in detail what Maynard Smith said but, as one of the world's leading scientists, it is inconceivable that he would have devoted more than a small proportion of his speech to such matters, if any. If he did, it certainly would not have been out of order."

In answer to the words of Wilder-Smith, "Subsequent efforts on the part of a librarian employed by the University of Oxford to obtain from the Oxford Union my address and a report on the debate were answered to the effect that it knew of no such debate ever having taken place and could give no information as to my person or even my present address," Dawkins wrote:

> That is utterly ridiculous. Such debates are a matter of record, and this debate was nothing out of the ordinary. The very idea that records were deliberately suppressed suggests a kind of paranoid vanity on Wilder-Smith's part. Why would anyone *want* to suppress anything so trivial as his name? Why would anyone be so naïve as to think you *could* suppress an event which was attended by hundreds of people, and very probably reported in the

university newspaper. If the library was unable to find some record or other, Wilder-Smith should simply have asked them to look again. Librarians do sometimes file things in the wrong place. Things go missing. When that happens, you look somewhere else. To conclude from the fact that somebody couldn't *find* something that there has been a conspiracy to *suppress* it is classic paranoia.

(Again, I would like to interject some comments. One is hard pressed to find any reference to this event except in Durant's faulty website and Dr. Wilder-Smith's book. I have contacted the Oxford Union and received the following response: "Your e-mail to the Union regarding the debate in 1986 has been forward (sic) on to me and I have been asked to get in touch. Unfortunately we won't have any of the information you require on the debate, indeed it sounds like you have more than we do. The only records kept of debates are the title, speakers' names and result. We don't hold any other information such as reports or fliers (there wouldn't have been any, only the title of the debate published in the term card). Unfortunately I can't even give you the result for this debate. The results are noted in a large minute book which spans several years. I'm sorry to say that the minute book in question was either lost or stolen many years ago, which is a great pity. I'm sorry the Union can't be of any help to you. If there is anything else though you feel I might be able to help with then please do not hesitate to get in touch.")

As to Dr. Dawkins' comment about paranoia, why did he himself feel compelled impassionedly to plea for a zero vote on the creation side? He used the notion of suppression four times and asked why would people be motivated to do this. The Apostle Paul offers an answer (Rom. 1:18). The facts seem to be that the record book is missing and the numbers in Durant's report are false. I am not in a position to judge who did what or when, but much of the information that is available to the public is misleading.

In my June 1 e-mail to Dr. Dawkins I also wrote, "Perhaps now I can better understand why you are reluctant to debate those who believe that life in all of its brilliance could not have come about by non-intelligent chance."

He responded: "If you seriously think that evolution is equivalent to 'non-intelligent chance' you have a lot of learning to do. May I recommend that you read something about evolution before making such ill-informed statements. I have devoted three of my books (*The Blind Watchmaker, River Out of Eden,* and *Climbing Mount Improbable*) to explaining that evolution by natural selection is the very opposite of a chance process."

Professor Dawkins also, apparently, does not allow that there are any sound scientific arguments on the creation side. I wrote him again offering to send him more than twenty (each condensed into a single paragraph) but he did not respond to this.

In summary, an Oxford Union Debate occurred on February 14, 1986. The Oxford Union has little if any memory of it. Despite Dr. Dawkins' plea, there were apparently 115 votes (possibly 150 votes[66]) for the creation position. 115 votes would be 37 percent; 150 votes, closer to 50 percent. This was done near Darwin's turf. Imagine flat-earthers going to NASA and convincing over 37% of the scientists there that the earth was flat. Creation science may not be as closely akin to flat-earthism as Dr. Dawkins supposes (see his *Free Inquiry* article [23 (1), 2003]).

Follow-Up

On June 18, 2003, I sent another e-mail message to Dr. Dawkins: "There apparently was an audio taping of the 1986 debate, and it is possible that I will be able to get a transcription of it in a month or so. I also have become aware of an article in *Origins* (May 1987, pp.10-11) that reports the outcome as 198 to 115. I have copied some of the *Origins* article below. Feel free to comment, but I remember that you said you were busy, etc.

> On Friday 14, February 1986 the Oxford Union Society (the debating society at Oxford University) held a Debate on the motion: "That the doctrine of creation is more valid than the theory of evolution." One of the speakers opposing the motion was Dr Richard Dawkins. David C. C. Watson was present and now comments on some of his arguments. RD: "The logical status of the evidence for the Theory of Evolution is just the same as the logical status of the evidence that the Roman Empire existed...." Comment: (a) There is no 'theory' that the Roman Empire existed. What has never been disputed as a fact does not require a theory to under-gird it, mainly because it depends on human testimony, which is also the basis of true science. If a man is found murdered, there may be twenty different theories based on circumstantial evidence; but if twenty people saw him murdered, and their testimony agrees, it is absurd to speak of the 'theory' of how he died. There were millions of eyewitnesses of the Roman Empire; thousands of them wrote about it, and hundreds of these writings have survived–books, letters, decrees and monuments. In broad outline, their testimonies agree. They could not possibly have been faked; the evidence is indisputable. By contrast, Darwin's

theory was hotly disputed from the day of its birth. Why? because nobody has ever observed macro-evolution in any country in any century in any shape or form—no fish becoming frogs, nor any of the fossils of the necessarily numerous transitional species.

Whereas I did received subsequent e-mail responses from Dr. Dawkins, I never received a specific response to this June 18, 2003 e-mail message from me.

Conclusion

Man is both fallible and precious at the same time. The Bible says that it is better to trust the Lord than to put confidence in man, but many people almost worship Dawkins. Many more worship Darwin. These men, however, like me, are/were fallible. We are, also, precious. Why? Because we are so noble? No. It is because (1) man is made in God's image and (2) God became a man to rescue us from our rebellion against Him. May the Lord Jesus Christ, who converted the Apostle Paul on the Damascus Road, be pleased to reach down in mercy to many like Dr. Dawkins and convert them to His grace and patient love.

Chapter 9

. . . .

SOMETHING MANY PEOPLE DO NOT REALIZE ABOUT JOSEPH STALIN

We jump now from England to Russia, but the connecting glue is still the infamous Englishman Charles Darwin. Some have the mistaken notion that faith and religion are linked inseparably with the confession of a supreme being, but many exercise faith in self and other human beings to the exclusion of the divine. This, too, is religion. Whatever serves as one's basic system of beliefs about his or her place and role in the universe is certainly a faith, a religion.

Joseph Stalin, though an atheist, was a believer. His was a faith resulting in tremendous brutality; nevertheless, it was a faith! What was it? Why did it result in death to millions? My purpose here is to offer some answers to these questions. I also add insights of the eminent authority on Russia's soul, Nobel laureate Alexander Solzhenitsyn.

What Was Stalin's Faith?

Often an individual's faith is firmly attached to a book of some kind. Muslims have the Koran; Hindus, their Veda;

and Christians, the Bible. Writings of Confucius, Buddha, and indeed, Mao Tse-Tung, serve similar purposes for other groups. In Stalin's case, the writings of Marx, Engels, and Lenin incited him, but to stop here would be premature. There is one man-book amalgam which may have been even more determinative for Stalin, especially during his youthful, impressionable years. The man was England's Charles Darwin; the book, his *The Origin of Species*.

To document this, appeal is made first to a book published in Moscow entitled, *Landmarks in the Life of Stalin*. It was written during Stalin's "glory," and was designed to set him in a positive light. Note in the selection cited, that faith in Darwin and his "book" contrasts markedly with faith in a supreme being: "At a very early age, while still a pupil in the ecclesiastical school, Comrade Stalin developed a critical mind and revolutionary sentiments. He began to read Darwin and became an atheist."

G. Glurdjidze, a boyhood friend of Stalin's, relates:

I began to speak of God, Joseph heard me out, and after a moment's silence, said: "You know, they are fooling us, there is no God...."

I was astonished at these words, I had never heard anything like it before. "How can you say such things, Soso?" I exclaimed.

"I'll lend you a book to read; it will show you that the world and all living things are quite different from what you imagine, and all this talk about God is sheer nonsense," Joseph said.

"What book is that?" I enquired.

"Darwin. You must read it," Joseph impressed on me[67]

A few pages later, another individual, also reflecting on Stalin's youthful pursuits, added the following: "… in order to disabuse the minds of our seminary students of the myth that the world was created in six days, we had to acquaint ourselves with the geological origin and age of the earth, and be able to prove them in argument; we had to familiarize ourselves with Darwin's teachings."

Had Marx, Engels, and Lenin Shared the Same Faith?

It has already been stated that Stalin was influenced by the writings of these men. Did this dilute the effect of Darwin on him, or were these men also affected by the same British naturalist? The answer to the second question must be affirmative. Conway Zirkle, Professor of Botany at the University of Pennsylvania, published a book in 1959 entitled, *Evolution, Marxian Biology, and the Social Scene*, in which he cites comments made in correspondence between Engels and Marx. As early as December 12, 1859 (only months after *The Origin of Species* was published), Friedrich Engels wrote to Karl Marx: "Darwin, whom I am just now reading, is splendid."[68]

About a year later (December 19, 1860), Marx, the Father of Communism, responded, "During my time of trial, these last few weeks, I have read all sorts of things; among others, Darwin's book of natural selection. Although it is developed in the crude English style, this is the book which contains the basis in natural history for our view."[69] To one, Ferdinand Lassalle, he wrote (January 16, 1861), "Darwin's book is very important and serves me as a basis in natural science for the class struggle in history."

Zirkle also indicated that Marx wanted to dedicate *Das Kapital* to Darwin. Harvard's Stephen Jay Gould, once an intense and recent spokesman for evolution, corroborated this by reporting that he saw Darwin's copy of Marx's first volume inscribed by Marx describing himself as a "sincere admirer" of the English naturalist.[70]

Ruis credits Vladimir Lenin with the following commentary on Darwin: "Darwin put an end to the belief that the animal and vegetable species bear no relation to one another, except by chance, and that they were created by God, and hence immutable."[71]

Was Stalin's Evolutionary Faith Really All That Brutal?

The 20th and the beginning of the 21st centuries have involved tyranny and mass genocide. One needs only to remember the two million Cambodians slaughtered under Pol Pot, the six million Jews exterminated by Adolf Hitler, and the forty million helpless lives aborted in America since 1973. Near the top of the list of atrocities, however, might well be the millions of Russian people eliminated under Stalin's murderous rule.

Harrison E. Salisbury of *The New York Times*, described the Soviet system of prison camps as "a whole continent of terror…. Compared with those who brought about the hundreds of thousands of executions and the millions of deaths in the Soviet terror system, the Czars seem almost benign…. Our minds boggle at the thought of a systematized, routine evil, under which three or four or more million men and women were sentenced each year to forced labor and eternal exile and in a manner so casual that the prisoners often were not even told what their sentences were...."[72]

"Men Have Forgotten God"

In 1983, Alexander I. Solzhenitsyn, winner of the 1970 Nobel Prize for Literature, gave an address in London in which he attempted to explain why so much evil had befallen his people:

> Over a half century ago, while I was still a child, I recall hearing a number of old people offer the following explanation for the great disasters that had befallen Russia: "Men have forgotten God; that's why all this has happened." Since then I have spent well-nigh fifty years working on the history of our revolution; in the process I have read hundreds of books, collected hundreds of personal testimonies, and have already contributed eight volumes of my own toward the effort of clearing away the rubble left by that upheaval. But if I were asked today to formulate as concisely as possible the main cause of the ruinous revolution that swallowed up some sixty million of our people, I could not put it more accurately than to repeat: "Men have forgotten God; that's why all this has happened."[73]

But did Solzhenitsyn consider any relationship involving Soviet oppression, Stalin's terror, and Darwin's theories on origin? In his towering book, *The Gulag Archipelago*, Solzhenitsyn recounts an incident which apparently took place in 1937-1938 at a district party conference meeting in Moscow province. The secretary (replacing an arrested one) was paying tribute to Comrade Stalin. The group, including the new secretary, was standing and applauding their esteemed leader. Even a single minute of feverish clapping consumes energy, but in this case it was important to sustain the "enthusiasm" much longer. Three, four, five minutes passed and more! Tired arms! But who could risk stopping? Seven, eight, and nine minutes elapsed. It was absurd! Finally after eleven minutes, a local factory director stopped clapping and sat down. All followed suit, but that night the one who stopped first was arrested and given ten years! He was told, "Don't ever be the first to stop applauding!" Solzhenitsyn queries, "And just what are we supposed to do? How are we supposed to stop?" In harmony with the position of this chapter, he added: "Now that's what Darwin's natural selection is. And that's also how to grind people down with stupidity."[74]

Conclusion

In chapter one, I documented that Hitler was a fanatical evolutionist. Evolutionary language and terms were shown to be used in his book. This chapter discusses Stalin, along with the Fathers of Communism. They were practical evolutionists, weeding out the unfit from their countries. The attachments of these men to Darwin have been made explicit, and, again, it would seem wise to include evolutionary explanations if we want fully to understand their actions. Of Hitler it may be said that he killed millions; of these men, and especially of Stalin, tens of millions!

Of course none of this proves or disproves the theory in and of itself. That is done elsewhere in this book. It does prove, however, that much evil has entered the world under the tutelage of Darwin's pathetic theory. Henry Fairfield Osborn, a famed American biologist, once wrote, "The ethical principle inherent in evolution is that only the best has a right to survive...."[75] This, however, is nonsense, but it is important for the reader to see the interconnectedness of all these chapter/tiles. The Lord Jesus Christ was concerned to heal the sick and deformed—not the "best" but the "least." He showed compassion for the weak and enfeebled. Not much of a follower of evolution's "ethical principle" was He, but, then again, one would hardly expect this from the Creator who derides foolish nonsense (Ps. 2:4; 59:8).

"Men have forgotten God;
that's why all this has happened."

Chapter 10

A Beautiful American Biologist

O ffensive words from one American biologist where displayed in the previous chapter, but we do not have to be ashamed of all American biologists. George Washington Carver was born a slave; his beginning was difficult. His mother, a widow, was taken from George while he was still an infant, and he himself was sickly. What possible value could such a life have? He was "owned" by Moses Carver and was known as Carver's George.

When George Carver got older and was about to enter high school, he added his middle initial. Someone else in town had his first and last names, and mail belonging to him was going to that other namesake. The young lad decided to give himself the middle initial, W, to distinguish himself from the other. When asked if it stood for Washington, he had no objection. Not wanting to be egotistical, however, he consistently signed his name with the diminutive, George W. Carver.

Despite difficulties, George Washington Carver did not waste his life. Rejected from one college because his skin color was thought to be too dark, he did not quit. Later in

life, he attended two colleges and was accepted as an assistant professor at one.

Most importantly, Dr. Carver loved his fellow humans
and God. There was a time when peanuts were thought to
have little value, and the South needed another crop besides
cotton. Dr. Carver, wanting to help his fellow man, discovered hundreds of valuable uses for peanuts. *Reader's Digest*
reported the following concerning his visit with Congressmen in Washington:

> He showed the Congressmen a peanut substitute for
> quinine, peanut foods for livestock, mock oysters and
> thirty different dyes. By now his time was up, but the
> Congressmen quickly voted him unlimited time to con-
> tinue. So, for nearly two hours, he held the committee
> spellbound as he showed still more of his products—van-
> ishing cream, rubbing oils, milk flakes —and answered
> questions about the peanut.[76]

> Representative Barkley asked, "How does it go in
> punch?"

> Carver said, "Well, I'll give you some punches! Here is
> one with orange, one with lemon and one with cherry.
> Here is instant coffee, which already has in it cream and
> sugar. Here is buttermilk, Worcestershire sauce, pick-
> les—all made from the peanut."

> Barkley added, "Where did you learn all this?" Carver,
> using words similar to but very different from Stalin,
> responded with: "From a book."

> Barkley followed, "What book?"

> Did Carver, like Stalin, point to Darwin's *Origin*? No. He
> answered, "The Bible. In Genesis we are told: 'Behold,
> I have given you every herb that bears seed on the face

of the earth, and every tree bearing seed. To you it shall be meat.'"

When, at last, the Congressmen let him go, every member of the committee rose and applauded him, and in the following year a tariff was placed on peanuts.

Dr. Carver also talked to God. He told about the following in a speech he gave at Macalester College in St. Paul, Minnesota:

Groping for solace that October day, he had walked through the predawn darkness of his beloved woodlands. As he searched for the first glimmer of the new morning, he cried out, "Oh, Mr. Creator, why did You make this universe?"

And the Creator answered me, "You want to know too much for that little mind of yours," He said, "Ask me something more your size."

So I said, "Dear Mr. Creator, tell me what man was made for."

Again He spoke to me: "Little man, you are still asking for more than you can handle. Cut down the extent of your request and improve the intent."

And then I asked my last question. "Mr. Creator, why did You make the peanut?"

"That's better!" the Lord said, and He gave me a handful of peanuts and went with me back to the laboratory and, together, we got down to work.

Inside the laboratory, Carver closed the door, pulled on an apron and shelled a handful of peanuts. That whole day and night, he literally tore the nuts apart, isolating their fats and gums, their resins and sugars and starches. Spread before him were pentoses, pentosans, legumins, lysin, amido and amino acids. He tested these in different combinations under varying degrees of heat and pressure, and soon his hoard of synthetic treasures began to grow: milk, ink, dyes, shoe polish, creosote, salve, shaving cream and, of course, peanut butter.

Continuing with *Reader's Digest*:

Thomas Edison once invited him to come work with him in the Edison laboratories in Menlo Park, New Jersey, at a minimum annual salary of $100,000. Carver declined the offer, as he had all the others, and seemed astonished that anyone expected him to claim rewards from the gifts God had given him. "But if you had all that money," he was once challenged, "you could help your people."

"If I had all that money," Carver replied, "I might forget about my people."

Students would come to hear Dr. Carver "talk of the relationship between science and the Scriptures. In time, the group swelled until finally it became so large that the informal discussions were scheduled as regular classes and shifted to the assembly room in the Carnegie Library. It was a rare week when all three hundred seats were not filled."

It was to this "Bible class" that Carver spoke some of his most pungent aphorisms: On cigarettes: "If God had intended the human nose to be used for a chimney, He would have turned our nostrils up." On nature: "I love to think of nature as an unlimited broadcasting system through which God speaks to us every hour, if we will only tune Him in."

130

To a class of seniors he said, "You may have to go into areas where the invisible 'Not Wanted' sign is up. But remember that this has happened before. It happened to a man called Jesus when He went to Galilee."

Here is a final quotation: "I have made it a rule to go out and sit...at four o'clock every morning and ask the good Lord what I am to do that day. Then I go ahead and do it."[77]

Dr. Carver died about six months after I was born. I never met him, but I hope to meet him someday in heaven and love him as a brother. I sorrow with his rejection, but I delight in his loving heart. As I and others face tomorrow, we would do well to follow Dr. Carver's example. When we get up in the morning, let us ask the Lord what He wants us to do that day, and then let us go and do it. Our lives are precious, too. Let us not waste them!

Chapter 11

SOMETHING PRESENTLY EXISTS IN AMERICA THAT IS FAR WORSE EVEN THAN SLAVERY!

I am an American by choice *and* by birth! But how can this be? I was born in Canada, part of North America (therefore, Canadians are Americans, too), but I became a citizen of the United States by choice. I am also happy that I am a citizen of this great land; nevertheless, there are significant blemishes—both in our collective past and in our collective present.

Slavery, Fostered by Evolution, Is One Such Blemish

Addressing Harriet Beecher Stowe, President Lincoln said, "So this is the little lady who made this big war." He was referring, of course, to the Civil War. Her tool was the worthy, historical novel, *Uncle Tom's Cabin*.

It is interesting to note that, though Stowe's book was written some seven years prior to the publication of Darwin's *On the Origin of Species*, there are perspectives contained in it that expose evolutionary thinking as evil. Evolution was around long before Charles Darwin borrowed

Rev. Josiah Henson, 1789-1883, apparently served as the historical personage behind the Uncle Tom character in Stowe's book.

the notion of natural selection from others (without giving proper credit)[78] and amplifying the "theory."

One of the more noble characters in Stowe's book is Augustine St. Clare, twin brother of the much less noble Alfred. This is what Augustine said about this less noble brother: "Alfred, who is as determined a despot as ever walked, does not pretend to this kind of defense; no, he stands, high and haughty, on that good old respectable ground, *the right of the strongest*; and he says, and I think quite sensibly, that the American planter is 'only doing, in another form, what the English aristocracy and capitalists are doing by the lower classes;' that is, I take it, *appropriating* them, body and bone, soul and spirit, to their use and convenience."[79]

This same character (a few pages earlier in the book) speaks of his father, who "considered the Negro, through

all possible gradations of color, as an intermediate link between man and animals, and graded all his ideas of justice
or generosity on this hypothesis."

Note that this "intermediate link between man and animals" is not unlike Hitler's "monstrosities halfway between
man and ape" and Darwin's "The break between man and
his nearest allies will then be wider, for it will intervene
between man in a more civilized state, as we may hope,
even than the Caucasian, and some ape as low as a baboon,
instead of as now between the Negro or Australian and the
gorilla" (cf. Chapter One).

In addition, the phrase, "Uncle Tom," has come to mean
something quite degrading and different from the main
character represented in Stowe's book. To illustrate, it would
be comparable to saying that Creator Christ was an Uncle
Tom because He meekly submitted to the humiliation and
indignity of the cross. But all Christians should know that
the Savior was a far greater warrior than even His forefather
David, who took down only one giant—Goliath. The Lord
of glory, by meekly submitting to the ignominy of the cross,
took on the world's greatest evils and won! He triumphed
over death, sin, Satan, and hell!

Correspondingly, the main character of Stowe's book,
first to own the *evolving* name Uncle Tom, stood up against
an evil incarnate, Simon Legree. To be sure, Tom willingly
laid down his life for fellow slaves, but he also gained the
victory! In other words, the character Uncle Tom was no
mere "Uncle Tom" in the derogatory sense! In addition, his
heart was huge, his love, magnanimous!

Tom was devoted to the Bible, and his language was "creationary" (as opposed to evolutionary). In offering counsel
to his young master, George Shelby, Stowe put these words
into the mouth of the valiant Uncle Tom: "Be a good Mas'r,
like yer father; and be a Christian, like yer mother. 'Member

135

yer Creator in the days o' yer youth, Mas'r George" (p. 112). Stowe's novel-documentary overflows with Scriptural allusions throughout, such as this one to Ecclesiastes 12:1.

According to Stowe, Uncle Tom practiced what he preached. Prior to most of his trials, his wife, Aunt Chloe, warned her husband of future trials. Listen to Tom's brief sermon to her: "I'm in the Lord's hands," said Tom; "nothin' can go no furder than he lets it; and thar's *one* thing I can thank him for. It's me that's sold and going down, and not you nur the chil'en. Here you're safe; what comes will come only on me; and the Lord, he'll help me, I know he will."

Returning to Augustine St. Clare, this twin shared why he himself had not yet submitted to becoming a Christian:

> "My view of Christianity is such," he added, "that I think no man can consistently profess it without throwing the whole weight of his being against this monstrous system of injustice that lies at the foundation of all our society; and, if need be, sacrificing himself in the battle. That is, I mean that I could not be a Christian otherwise, though I have certainly had intercourse with a great many enlightened and Christian people who did no such thing; and I confess that the apathy of religious people on this subject, their want of perception of wrongs that filled me with horror, have engendered in me more skepticism than any other thing."

Stowe's "monstrous system" reminds me again of Hitler's "monstrosities halfway between man and ape." The world came to know just how monstrous was Hitler's system. America's slavery system was also monstrous, but...

136

Another Present-Day American System Is Even More Monstrous!

Applying Stowe's words to modern times, it is sad indeed that there is now another evil in America that is every bit as evil as slavery. An estimated 30 percent of Americans align with the evil of "partial birth abortion," but Creator Christ Himself sanctified life in the womb, living there Himself for nine months. Imagine the thought of some modern medical practitioner going back in time to Bethlehem, repositioning the Lord's body in Mary's womb so that feet would appear first, leading every part of the body out except the head, inserting an instrument into the base of Jesus' skull, sucking out His brain, pulling out the infant corpse, and then asking for a $5,000 reward! Slavery was and is evil, but at least some slaves lived! Forty million unborn children have been slaughtered in America since 1973!

The connection of this evil to evolution is exposed in the next chapter, but this new evil, not prevalent during the Civil War, does not allow a child even to see the light of day! American babies are slaughtered by the millions; moreover, twice as many non-white babies are aborted as white babies![80]

Good Still Exists in America

Before explaining the connection of evolution to abortion, however, let me hold out hope to the reader. Good still exists in America. There are modern-day Harriet Beecher Stowes reaching out in love to women in crisis pregnancy situations—providing support, loving care, clothing, and encouragement to young mothers and their rescued children.[81] Stowe uplifted Christian love a century and a half ago. One passage, involving such an acceptance of George

Harris (another main character of the book) is worth quoting. He had been escaping from slavery and had just been reunited to his heroic wife, Eliza, and their child (both also escaping from slavery). It reads as follows: "This, indeed was a home—home—a word that George had never yet known a meaning for; and a belief in God, and trust in his providence, began to encircle his heart, as, with a golden cloud of protection and confidence, dark, misanthropic, pining, atheistic doubts, and fierce despair, melted away before the light of a living Gospel, breathed in living faces, preached by a thousand unconscious acts of love and goodwill, which, like the cup of cold water given in the name of a disciple, shall never lose their reward."

We will see in the next chapter that Margaret Sanger, the founder of Planned Parenthood, was a practical evolutionist. Her legacy is that a disproportionate number of babies of color are slaughtered in American "abortuaries."

Conclusion

Something far worse than a Civil War is ahead. Secular fundamentalists in America's "highest" institutions continue to promote the godless, evolutionary religion of secular humanism in the guise of science, but the Lord of Harriet Beech Stowe, Science Incarnate, is very much alive, having conquered death, and is returning to this planet some day! Jesus Christ, the same yesterday, today, and forever, "cometh to judge the earth" (Ps. 96:13). Unrepentant secularists will experience Him as a consuming fire! May, by God's grace, many repent. The Bible says, "Kiss the Son, lest He be angry, and ye perish from the way, when His wrath is kindled but a little. Blessed are all they that put their trust in Him" (Ps. 2:12 KJV).

Chapter 12

SUBTLE SANGER

We read in the Bible that Satan disguises himself as an angel of light, and Margaret Sanger, the founder of Planned Parenthood (a major promoter of abortions in America today), fooled many people, too. The purpose of this chapter is to expose her evolutionary connection and to warn America of an evil greater than slavery.

Sanger, far more subtle than Hitler, was also a practicing evolutionist,[82] and many people today do not seem to realize that the same poisonous philosophy (evolutionism) that justified killing under Hitler has also infected the American abortion mentality.

According to documents released as recently as February 10, 1992, "Joseph Mengele, the Auschwitz death-camp doctor known as the 'Angel of Death' for his experiments on inmates, practiced medicine in Buenos Aires for several years in the 1950s. He 'had a reputation as a specialist in abortions,' which were illegal."[83] It should not be surprising that one who extinguished life at Auschwitz would practice a similar grisly crusade on life in the womb. Abortionists may not like this comparison with Nazism, but abortion under Hitler's Mengele and abortion under the watchful eye of American doctors is bloody either way. Murdering human beings is among the worst of sins!

America's Carl Sagan Tried to Justify Abortion-Murder

Carl Sagan encouraged the fiction that life in the womb traces an evolutionary history. We "must decide," he wrote, "what distinguishes a human being from other animals and when, during gestation, the uniquely human qualities—whatever they are—emerge."[84] He compared the appearance of the developing embryo to "a segmented worm" and added that "something like the gill arches of a fish or an amphibian ... become conspicuous, and there is a pronounced tail." The face becomes "reptilian ... (then) somewhat pig-like." Eventually, it "resembles a primate's but is still not quite human."

In the article, evolutionary thinking offers yet again "justification" for extinguishing life thought to be subhuman. This, of course, is pseudo-science and nonsense. The science of genetics has confirmed that the embryo is identifiably human from the moment of conception.

Sanger Did Reveal, Believe It or Not, Some Pro-Life Tendencies.

Margaret Sanger (1879-1966) has been given the unusual title, "Father of Modern Society."[85] Her evolutionary mentality will be documented below, but first there should be a consideration of her views relating to abortion.

In her *Woman and the New Race*, Sanger offered a conflicting message about this issue. On the one hand she wrote, "I assert that the hundreds of thousands of abortions performed in America each year are a disgrace to civilization."[86] Pro-lifers would heartily agree! She even referred to "babies" in the womb—not using the now politically correct term, *fetuses*: "There will be no killing of babies in the womb by abortion."

Her message was inconsistent, however. Not only did Linda Gordon, author of *Woman's Body, Woman's Right*, a major work dealing with the history of birth control in America, indicate that Margaret Sanger "defended women's rights to abortion,"[87] Sanger herself, in the very volume denouncing abortion already cited, wrote, "The most merciful thing that the large family does to one of its infant members is to kill it." This hardly sounds pro-life.

Whatever may be said of her inconsistent views, Sanger's legacy is an organization that certainly encourages and participates in the killing of millions of, to use her phrase, America's "infant members." What was it about her philosophy that allowed for this?

Like Hitler, Sanger Sought to Impose Practical Evolutionism on the Populace

Hitler's link to evolution has already been documented. He put survival-of-the-fittest into action, and millions of "unfit" people died as a result. I believe that something comparable to what happened under the leadership of Hitler is happening now in America. "Babies in the womb," most of them healthy and fit, have been slaughtered by the tens of millions in the United States of America—four thousand every day!

What some may not realize is that the same poisonous philosophy that infected Hitler also influenced Margaret Sanger. She said Charles Darwin observed "that we do

141

not permit helpless human beings to die off, but we create philanthropies and charities, build asylums and hospitals and keep the medical profession busy preserving those who could not otherwise survive." Her view was that such philanthropies and charities were "ameliorative" at best, and that some so-called benevolences were "positively injurious to the community and the future of the race."

Her following words (content-wise) sound like they could have been spoken by Adolf Hitler himself: "The most serious charge that can be brought against modern 'benevolence' is that it encourages the perpetuation of defectives, delinquents and dependents. These are the most dangerous elements in the world community, the most devastating curse on human progress and expression."

One wonders how far Sanger would like to have taken her eugenics. She reported a study of the United States Army and concluded that "nearly half—47.3 percent—of the population had the mentality of twelve-year-old children or less—in other words, that they were morons."[88]

On the racial dimension, Linda Gordon (cf. above) quotes from a letter written by Margaret Sanger to Clarence Gamble on October 19, 1939: "We do not want word to go out that we want to exterminate the Negro population and the minister is the man who can straighten out the idea if it ever occurs to any of their more rebellious members." Many years prior, Sanger said, "Whether or not the white races will be ultimately wiped off the face of the earth depends, to my mind, largely upon the conduct and behavior of the white people themselves. (Applause.)"[89]

Birth control for Sanger was "nothing more or less than the facilitation of the process of weeding out the unfit." A eugenist, she defined the field as "the attempt to solve the problem from the biological and evolutionary point of view." She wanted to change things "to the construction and evolution of humanity itself." She advocated applying "a stern and rigid policy of sterilization and segregation to that grade of population whose progeny is already tainted, or whose inheritance is such that objectionable traits may be transmitted to offspring."[90] Revealing pro-choice tendencies, she went on to promote the notion of giving "certain dysgenic groups in our population their choice of segregation or sterilizations."

Ms. Sanger assumed "the evolutionary process of man"[91] and argued that the "intelligence of a people is of slow evolutional development." She hoped for a motherhood that would refuse "to bring forth weaklings." Such a motherhood "withholds the unfit brings forth the fit." She wrote of "woman's upward struggle" and described the "lack of balance between the birth rate of the 'unfit' and the 'fit'" as "the greatest present menace to civilization."

Like Stalin, Sanger Chose Darwin over Jesus

As has been mentioned, the Lord Jesus Christ sanctified life in the womb by living there Himself for nine months (Isa. 49:5, cf. Luke 1:35). He also created every womb that was ever made (John 1:3). As the promised "seed" of the woman (Gen. 3:15), He came to rescue daughters (like those for whom Margaret Sanger expressed concern throughout her writings) from their burdens of pain, suffering, sin, and death. He came to set them free (John 8:36), and many women would testify that they have indeed been set free and will be set free even from death.

Sanger, however, wrote of a different Jesus, "a Jesus who (would) not die upon the cross." In place of the real Jesus who understands suffering intimately, she chose the hollow shell of evolutionary "science." Sadly, she wrote, "Interest in the vague sentimental fantasies of extra-mundane existence, in pathological or hysterical flights from the realities of our earthiness, will have through atrophy disappeared, for in that dawn men and women will have come to the realization … that here close at hand is our paradise, our everlasting abode, our Heaven and our eternity."

But how is Margaret Sanger qualified to make such pronouncements? Her present bodily "abode" is very undesirable (coffin? charred remains?), but Jesus is alive with a resurrected body in heaven! After He was resurrected, He proclaimed, "I am He that liveth, and was dead; and, behold, I am alive for evermore, Amen; and have the keys of hell and of death" (Rev. 1:18).

Some might object, "Who does Jesus think He is— God?"

Precisely! Moreover, Jesus made a far greater impact on this earth than Sanger. Why should anyone listen to Sanger over Him? His teachings about the future, contrary to Margaret Sanger's preachings, were neither "vague sentimental fantasies" nor "pathological," and they will never "atrophy." Heaven and earth may pass—but His words will never pass away (Matt. 24:35). He emphatically said, "I am the resurrection, and the life: he that believeth in me, though he were dead, yet shall he live: And whosoever liveth and believeth in me shall never die" (John 11:25-26).

Conclusion

The evolutionary mentality behind abortion is bad science and leads to bad ethics. On the positive side, Margaret Sanger did encourage attention to a very important subject—to what she called "the titanic strength of the sexual instinct." Indirectly, she was affirming the scriptural truth that "love is strong as death; jealousy is cruel as the grave … Many waters cannot quench love, neither can the floods drown it: if a man would give all the substance of his house for love, it would utterly be condemned" (Song of Solomon 8:6-7).

She also sought to promote birth control. The ultimate need, however, is for Holy Spirit control. The Lord Jesus Christ, after receiving from the Father the promise of the Holy Spirit, shed Him forth upon the earth for the benefit of His followers (Acts 2:33). The only way an unbeliever can experience this loving presence and control is to bow the heart in repentance and faith before the Sovereign Creator-Savior, Jesus Christ.

Chapter 13

DARWIN GOT "HIS" KEY THOUGHT FROM A CREATIONIST!

The only degree that Darwin ever received was in theology, and there is significant evidence that the key ingredient in his evolutionary theory, natural selection, came not from a fellow evolutionist but from a devout creationist! According to Loren C. Eiseley, formerly Benjamin Franklin Professor of Anthropology and the History of Science at the University of Pennsylvania, "the leading tenets of Darwin's work—the struggle for existence, variation, natural selection, and sexual selection—are *all fully expressed*" in a paper written by creationist Edward Blyth in 1835[92] (emphasis added). Unlike Darwin, however, Blyth saw natural selection as a preserving factor rather than as "a potentially liberalizing" one. According to this under-appreciated naturalist, the conserving principle was "intended by Providence to keep up the typical qualities of a species." Atypical variations, to use Eiseley's words, led to the animal's "discovery and destruction."[93]

Eiseley, not a creationist, wrote that "Blyth is more than a Darwinian precursor; he is, instead, a direct intellectual forebear...." In Eiseley's estimation, Blyth "belongs in the

royal line ... one of the forgotten parents of a great classic."
On the same page, Eiseley also charged that "Darwin made
unacknowledged use of Blyth's work."[94]

Editor Kenneth Heuer concluded, "this is Eiseley's discovery." Darwin had "failed to acknowledge his obligation
to Blyth."[95] He did acknowledge others (and even Blyth
peripherally), but, as Eiseley demonstrates persuasively,
Darwin for some reason chose not to credit creationist Blyth
with the key element in his theory—natural selection.

In addition to providing the reader with a chapter on
Edward Blyth written by contemporary Arthur Grote, Dr.
Eiseley furnished essays written by the creationist himself—
essays that most assuredly were read by Charles Darwin.
They originally appeared in *The Magazine of Natural History*
in 1835, 1836, and 1837. Examples of how this naturalist
honored his Creator are provided below.

In the first, *The Varieties of Animals* (pp. 97–111), Blyth
considered, among other things, changes in animal coloration. The mountain hare, for example, becomes white in
winter, "hardly to be discerned upon the snow." On the same
page Blyth wrote: "There has been, strangely enough, a difference of opinion among naturalists, as to whether these
seasonal changes of color were intended by Providence as
an adaptation to change of temperature, or as a means of
preserving the various species from the observation of their
foes, by adapting their hues to the color of the surface....
The fact is, they answer both purposes; and they are among
those striking instances of design, which so clearly and
forcibly attest the existence of an omniscient great First
Cause."[96]

It is sad that such language would be disallowed from
many if not all nature journals today—especially if written
by a living naturalist. It is refreshing, however, to read of a
naturalist who credits the Creator with concern for His crea-

tures. Words of the Creator Himself come to mind: "Then said the LORD, Thou hast had pity on the gourd, for the which thou hast not labored, neither madest it grow; which came up in a night, and perished in a night: And should not I spare Nineveh, that great city, wherein are more than six score thousand persons that cannot discern between their right hand and their left hand; *and also much cattle*?" (Jonah 4:10-11 KJV, emphasis added.)

Blyth's next essay[97] reveals a naturalist's heart bent in reverence before his Creator:

> It is the grand and beautiful, the sublime and comprehensive system which pervades the universe, of which the sun and planets are but a portion, and which, to return to ornithology, is so well exemplified in the adaptation of the ptarmigan to the mountain top, and the mountain top to the habits of the ptarmigan; which suits the ostrich to the arid desert, the woodpecker to the forest, and the petrel to "the far sea wave." It is the majestic and admirable system by which all nature works so beautifully together, and to which all that our external senses reveal appertains. It is the system which, exquisite and intensely interesting in all its minutest details, is, if possible, even more so in its complicated relation; by which, by the *unity of design* pervading which, all is demonstrable to be the workmanship of one omnipotent and all-foreseeing providence, under the beneficent dispensation of whom naught that ever exists or occurs stands isolated and alone, but all conduce and work admirably together for the benefit of the whole; by whose all-wise decree it is ordained, that, while the lofty and sterile mountain peak *attracts* the clouds, which in winter, in consequence, precipitate themselves upon it in the form of snow, it should *cause* itself to become clad in the hue of all others the most calculated to prevent its internal temperature from be-

ing farther reduced, and itself from thereby becoming an increased source of cold by radiation to all around; while, at the same time, the concretion of snow itself, instead of deluging the country round with superfluous moisture, is thus retained for a time upon the heights, not only to shelter the more tender organized productions of the mountain from severer cold, but also to furnish, by the action of the summer sun, a due supply of water, when needed, to the fountains and rills which irrigate and fertilize the more level country; there having done its part, to flow on to the mighty reservoirs of the ocean, again to arise in clouds, and to fulfill again its appointed rounds, with perpetual never ceasing energy, while the world endures.[98]

Dr. Eiseley wrote that "Edward Blyth was one to remember the color and shape of a darting bird or a fox going over a hedge. He saw things hiding, shifting, changing. He had what today we would call a photographic memory."[99] He also stated explicitly that Blyth was "a special creationist."[100]

An evolutionist himself, Eiseley viewed Blyth as laboring under an "eighteenth-century limitation upon organic divergence which blinded so many early nineteenth-century thinkers."[101] Who really are the blind, however? Geneticists know that there are definite boundaries to divergence. Try as they might, evolutionists cannot change one species into a viable other; they still have blind trust that it occurred many times in the past, however.

In Blyth's third essay, *Psychological Distinctions between Man and Other Animals*, the author wrote that animals "evince superhuman wisdom, because it is innate, and therefore, instilled by an all-wise Creator. Indeed, the unpremeditated resource of animals, in cases of emergency, is oftentimes decidedly superior to that of man; and why?

Because they need not experience for their guide, but are prompted to act by intuition."

Again, how very out-of-place these words would seem if appearing in secular publications today! Evolution is a religion for many, and departures from this godless orthodoxy are not generally tolerated. Reference to the "all-wise Creator" violates the godless orthodoxy of evolution.

The apostle Paul wrote long ago that men wickedly suppress the truth.[102] Why Darwin did not credit Edward Blyth more generously may not be known by us until He who unlocks the secrets of men's hearts returns and exposes all. Eiseley made a strong case, however, that Darwin benefited from Blyth especially in one key area but apparently chose not to credit the naturalist for this key insight.

Dr. Henry M. Morris wrote, "Although he was bound to know of the natural-selection writings of both Paley and Blyth, Darwin gave them no credit for their contribution to his own misuse of their perfectly appropriate use of natural selection."[103] One could conjecture that Darwin, knowing Blyth to be a special creationist, did not want to associate his doctrine with anything that could be understood within a creationist framework of thought.

Creationists have had and still have little problem with the tenets of natural selection. Small variations having survival benefit within created kinds, such as coloration of peppered moths or differently shaped beaks, no more disprove creation than fossils in sedimentary rocks disprove a universal flood. The Creator not only displays tremendous variety of kinds but also enormous variety within created kinds. How to transmute from one species to another is the problem, however. It was impossible for Darwin to get past that barrier, and it is just as impossible today.

As has been noted, Blyth wrote of an "all-wise Creator" and the "omniscient great First Cause." This Creator and

151

First Cause, the Lord Jesus Christ, will return someday and reveal what has been hidden. He said, "Fear them not therefore: for there is nothing covered, that shall not be revealed; and hid, that shall not be known."[104] The Bible says "Therefore judge nothing before the time, until the Lord come, who both will bring to light the hidden things of darkness, and will make manifest the counsels of the hearts.[105] Neither is there any creature that is not manifest in His sight: but all things are naked and opened unto the eyes of Him with whom we have to do."[106]

As Blyth intimates, however, the Creator is also compassionate in His dealings. Not only does He make it possible for animals to adapt "as a means of preserving the various species from the observation of their foes," as Blyth wrote (above), but He supremely extended Himself in love and compassion toward us who are made in His image. Knowing our rebellious hearts, He bore our sins on the cross, giving us a covering—His cloak of pure righteousness.

May the greatest Naturalist, who arrays the flowers of the field with more glory than that of Solomon, touch many more hearts, not only with the wonders of His intricate creation, but also with the preciousness of His bounteous love.

Chapter 14

* *

"DOESN'T GEOLOGY PROVE EVOLUTION?"

I had finished teaching a four-hour college evening course when I decided to stop into the skilled nursing facility to check in on my mother, who had just recently been released from HUP (Hospital of the University of Pennsylvania). Soon after I arrived, I sensed that things were going downhill and alerted the staff. They discovered that Mother's oxygen-saturation levels were critically low. An ambulance was called for, and I pumped Mother's manual respirator as she was being wheeled to an ambulance. I am not a trained medic, but I suspect that Mother might not have survived the night had I not been present. One, also, does not need to be a trained geologist to discuss geology.

Frank Zindler, Editor of the *American Atheist*, and I carried on a correspondence that lasted over four months.[107] Many issues were discussed, but by agreement there was a focus on two. One[108] was geological and may be put in the form of a question. Do the varves of the Green River Formation (near the Rocky Mountains) disprove the chronology of the Bible? Mr. Zindler was of the opinion that they did. I strongly disagreed.

He wrote, "But the whole question of astronomical time is rendered unimportant by the fact that we have evidence right here on earth that rules out absolutely the biblical chronology and shows that the earth ... has existed through long periods of time. I refer to the Green River Shale of Eocene age out in the Rocky Mountain area."

He also drafted the following: "In the case of the Green River Shale, the number of annual layers (not true varves, however, in their formation) extends to about three million.... I have repeatedly challenged such apologists to explain how, if these delicate layers (about 80 pairs of black/white layers per cm) are *not* annual layers, such delicate layered deposits (in the case of the Green River shale extending over thousands of square miles) could have been formed during a world-destroying flood, the ferocity of which biblical apologists never fail to require at various other parts of their 'theory.'"[109]

This rock illustrating varves from the Green River area is part of the author's collection.

Biblical Guidance

The Apostle Peter wrote, "But in your hearts set apart Christ as Lord. Always be prepared to give an answer to everyone who asks you to give the reason for the hope that you have. But do this with gentleness and respect" (1 Pet. 3:15). This does not mean that Christians have to become experts in everything, but loving the Lord with our minds may include doing more study than we had planned. The Lord Himself set an example of answering antagonistic questions.[110]

Everyone has a faith in something. If it is not in God, then it is in self or something else. Frank Zindler's faith was/is in evolution. He wrote that "we must never lose sight of the fact that all of science nowadays interlocks to produce a picture of evolution, from the cosmic level to the social level."[111] In the same context, he wrote, "The geneticist Dobzhansky once said that nothing in biology makes sense apart from evolution. The truth of that statement is everywhere evident."

My response at the time was as follows: "If I'm not mistaken, the founder of genetics opposed Darwin's theory. Several years ago, my wife had hairy cell leukemia. Her hematologist let me see the hairy cells in his microscope. I asked him if there was ever a time in human development when the blood is something other than human. (Sagan had suggested in an article I read that humans go through evolutionary stages during development, justifying abortion[112]). He contacted an authority at the University of Pennsylvania. The answer was that the notion is silly. Human blood is always human. It seems to me that evolutionary thinking might actually retard increased understanding about human blood. Here is biology that makes sense without evolution."[113]

My correspondent did not see his attitude about the Green River varves as a faith, however. He wrote, "It certainly is not 'faith' that accepts the reality of the millions of laminae in the GRS—laminae which by any imaginable means of formation requires more time than is allowed by the biblical chronology. This is science, not religion. This is acceptance of evidence, not belief based on faith (which Webster defines as 'unquestioning belief that does not require proof or evidence')."[114]

Does the Green River Shale Formation Point to Long Ages?

I may have been tentative when I was pumping air into my mother's lungs (first paragraph of this chapter), but I am glad I tried. My early responses to Frank Zindler were also somewhat tentative. At the time, I did not know much about this formation and wrote, "In Wyoming, the Mowry Shale contains an abundance of fish scales. How do we account for the tremendous number of fish scales unless we consider much water? Fish scales generally do not fossilize. Again, flooding is suggested. The Green River fish fossil shown to me by my colleague also points to significant water deposition."[115] I added a conjecture about the so-called varves: "Many years ago, following massive flooding and major ice-sheeting in northern (and southern) regions, the earth, seeking as it were to attain thermo-equilibrium, started to melt the ice. Edges of the ice sheets receded slowly north (and south). What we know today as the Green River Formation was involved in this process. With the melting came trauma to land. Canyons were formed rapidly (when massive amounts of water broke through natural, ice dams—cf. *Smithsonian* article[116]."

My associate in writing objected: "Now the idea that the GRS is post-glacial is utterly impossible. Even without recourse to radiometric dating ... the simple laws of sedimentary superposition show that the GRS was deposited long before the Pleistocene Epoch. Also, the nature of glacial outwash deposits is well studied (I myself have studied them in the field) and no competent geologist could possibly confuse them with varves. Also, you couldn't form layers of fish—scales or insect wings from glacial outwash—or with Noah's Flood either, for that matter."[117]

Surfing the Internet, I learned of Dr. Paul Buchheim, a professor of geology. He was kind enough to send some papers he had written concerning his own studies in the field. One abstract offers the following:

LAMINAE COUNTS WITHIN A SYNCHRONOUS OIL SHALE UNIT: A CHALLENGE TO THE VARVE CONCEPT BUCHHEIM, H. Paul, and BIAGGI, Robert, Department of Geological Sciences, Loma Linda University, Riverside, CA. 92515:

Many workers have interpreted the thin laminae common to "oil shales" of the Eocene Green River Formation as varves. However, laminae number and thickness studies of one unit in the formation near Kemmerer, Wyoming provide evidence to the contrary. One particular unit, dubbed the "Lower Sandwich Horizon" or "LSWH" was discovered to vary in thickness from 8.3 to 22.6 cm between localities spaced up to 15 kilometers apart. The laminae number of this unit varies from 1160 to 1568, with an overall increase of laminae number (up to 35%) and laminae thickness from basin center to margin. Kerogen content decreases from basin center to margin. Kerogen poor samples are more thickly laminated (.11- .19 mm) whereas kerogen rich samples are thinly laminated (.07). The LSWH is bounded top and bottom by two easily mappable tuffs about 2-3 cm thick. The tuffs represent time-synchronous units and theoretically the same exact amount of time is represented between them at all locations, no matter how many laminae there is between them or how thick the unit be.

The differences in laminae count, laminae thickness, unit thickness, and kerogen content can be accounted for by a model evoking more voluminous sedimentation and more frequent sedimentation "events" nearer the lake margins than center. The varve model is not adequate to explain these differences because it would predict the same number of laminae lake-wide as well as consistent unit thicknesses and kerogen content.[118]

I contacted other authorities as well. What follows is a summary response on my part to Frank Zindler about the Green River varves:

1. This issue is important. You have faith that it disproves biblical chronology. It is my purpose here to help you see why it does not. I realize you view this as an impossible assignment.

2. You also do not like the term, faith, as used above, but when you get into an airplane, you have faith (not certainty) that it will take you to your destination. This is the kind of thing I mean. The plane may crash, and I believe your confidence (faith) that your understanding of varves is accurate will crash sooner or later.

3. I have done several things to look into the varve matter more thoroughly. I share below some of my findings, but there are still some pending matters which may subsequently come in. Michael J. Oard,

for example, has written on the subject, but I have not yet checked into this. It's apparently in the Sept. '92 issue of the *Creation Research Society Quarterly* (pp.120-126). I may have it, but I am not sure where it is.

4. One of the things that had been pending was my e-mail letter to Dr. John Baumgardner. I was hoping I would get a response from him, and I did. About two years ago, you may have seen the article that was in *U.S. News and World Report* (June 16, 1997, p.55ff) about this scientist entitled, "The Geophysics of God." It says Dr. Baumgardner is "the world's pre-eminent expert in the design of computer models for geophysical convection, the process by which the earth creates volcanoes, earthquakes, and the movement of the continental plates." He got his master's in EE from Princeton and a PhD in geophysics from UCLA. I asked him if he had any insights about the GRF varves. On Fri., Jul 16, he responded:

One needs to consider the geological record as a whole and ask what does it tell us, and similarly with the Bible. I claim the geological record is literally screaming out: global water catastrophe! And the Bible likewise indicates the primary geological event since the creation of life on the planet is a global Flood. One then needs to approach the Green River Formation with this context in view. In terms of the Genesis flood, the Eocene in my assessment falls within the time of regression of the flood waters from the continents. The varve-like laminae would then have to be produced by rapid sedimentation

159

with rapid oscillations/wavelike conditions modulating the sedimentation process. A period of several seconds is sufficiently short to generate the number of laminae in the time available. One thing I can guarantee is that the evolutionary sedimentation rate of ten microns per year will bury and fossilize not a single one of the billions to trillions of beautifully preserved fish to be found today in the Green River sediments. I hope these brief remarks are helpful.

I wrote that Dr. Baumgardner's view is less complicated than mine. He sees the laminae as forming over much shorter periods than my model. Instead of six or seven laminae per year (my model), he sees them forming as a result of water regression, modulating wave motion over relatively flat surfaces, in mere seconds. I like it. I realize you probably radically disagree with his view. You probably want him to account for what you view as the dual-aspect of the laminae, but there are two responses I have to this. First, the smaller picture must fit into the larger (not the other way around). Second, the impression I have from the reading is that the laminae of the GRF are not classical varves; the dual aspect is not as clearly defined.

5. On Monday, September 19, I received another response from a practicing geologist, Carl Froede. He does not completely agree with Dr. Baumgardner's approach; he does agree, however, "that the 'varves' were catastrophically formed." His approach is ...

"post-flood land-locked lakes which were fed by the wet weather conditions of a post-flood Ice Age (I wrote about a similar setting for Lake Manly in

Death Valley a while back)." He added, "Volcanism which occurred during this time added 'layers' to these slowly subsiding saline lakes. Over time and with more water the lakes turned 'fresh.' The varves are a function of clay flocculation, dynamic compaction, and pH and Eh changes which occurred as the lakes turned from saline to fresh. The high acidity or alkalinity of the volcanic ash layers (they do vary even today) also played into producing these varves. This is my guess at this time."

An additional comment may be instructive. When I e-mailed Froede, I did not reveal your name. So his following comments are general in nature. He wrote, "You will *never* convince anyone of our biblical position (i.e., young-earth, global flood, the need for a Savior, etc.) unless they receive Jesus as their Lord first. I have shut my non-believing uniformitarian 'friends' up and had them admit that I was just as 'right' as they were, but they have *never* agreed with me about the flood or the biblical approach. They are blind (willfully!)." (Added comment from me: Please consider that man's problem is not as much an intellectual one as an ethical one. Man, in his pride, is in rebellion against God. Repentance and faith in Jesus is the only hope. Darwin did not conquer death. You and I face death. Jesus' tomb is empty. I pray to Him daily. He has flooded my life with overflowing delights. Sure, there are struggles, but He answers prayer. If you want more about answered prayer, let me know.)

6. "Have you heard of Guy Berthault, a French sedimentologist?" I wrote. He reported that the Bijou-Creek flood in Colorado ('65) produced twelve

161

feet of sediment in forty-eight hours and that 90-95 percent of the sediment had "horizontal laminated strata." A hundred years from now, a person looking at the horizontal laminated strata from the BCF might conclude old age, but the reality was forty-eight hours! This, to my way of thinking, gives some independent support to Dr. Baumgardner's words (above).[119]

7. I've looked at some videos. One of them, *Evidences—the Record of the Flood*, is very good. It produces scientific evidence for the flood, and a lot of the evidence is in the region surrounding the GRF and south to the Grand Canyon. If you haven't seen it, I highly recommend it. Apparently there is much evidence of turbidity formations and salt-water shells, suggestive that ocean water once covered much of the West. Have you heard about these items? Let me know if you would like to see one or two of these videos.

8. Back to the GRS formation; we are talking about something that is 27,500 feet thick...? If so, then we are talking about layering that is twice the height of the Grand Tetons! I've also seen Mt. McKinley. It's huge, but it's still less than 27,500 feet. You use the vast size of the GRF to prove (in your mind) an earth millions of years old, but this is very unusual layering. It does not exist all around the globe. It is massive. One mechanism that could account for such massive deposition is massive flooding on a massive scale. You say the flood does not fit the detailing of the layers, but this detailing may be mostly post-flood. A tremendous amount of the

massive layering, however, came about as a result of the flood. Some of the layers may even be pre-flood. Then the flood came with turbidities. After the flood came the influences of glaciation, water melt, glacial dams, breaking of the same, etc. The detailed laminae are not real varves (even you concede this). My thinking (and I wrote most of this before receiving the e-mail from Dr. Baumgardner) goes something like this:

Further to the north (Canada), there were ice sheets (remnant glaciers following flood trauma). During warmer days, the ice would melt and fill streams which ran for some distance over land and eventually into large, but shallow, lake-basins. During cooler periods, the stream water diminished significantly because the ice sheet melting diminished. This would result in thin layering. Correspondingly, during hot spells, there would be significant ice melting. The ice flow would increase the size of smaller streams and "push" fish and other organisms into the filling lake basin. The fish, etc. would live for a while but die when the cycle changed—there being a lag between the initial melting of ice and the arrival of stream water to the lake basins. As the water in the basins became too shallow, organisms would die. They became fossilized in the shallow (muddy) water. With the return of a hot spell, the cycle would start again—melt, full streams, a push to the lake, lake life, drying shallow-lake death, lamination, recycling, etc. During the summer, there could be multiple laminations. Some of them could be true varves. Over a long period, significant layering would build up. (As I said, most of this was written before the arrival of Dr. B's e-mail. Maybe it could be seen as an alternate to his. I will grant that my approach is probably vastly inferior to his.)

9. I've been around long enough to know that even the pro's can miss important details. We are dealing with something that is somewhat of a mystery. None of us were around when much of this happened. Let us say there are a thousand pieces to this "picture" puzzle, and we may have only fifty or sixty pieces in hand. PhD geologists may have ninety or one hundred, but they still have only about 10 percent of the data. In other words, they can have pieces in the wrong places. For you to suggest that I abandon my confidence in the historical accuracy of the Bible because I cannot explain everything about the GRS formation (or submit to some subjective and potentially faulty geological interpretation about the GRS) is, to my way of thinking, silly. (I am not insulting your intelligence here; I believe you are quite intelligent. But sometimes even intelligent people can make silly decisions. The final chapter on the GRF has not been written.)

10. You wrote, "The GRS laminae alternate in thickness patterns that follow the eleven-year sunspot cycle and higher cycles such as that of the precession of the equinoxes." I am very skeptical about this and am confident that real geology has not gotten to this level of refinement. You may have faith that it has; I do not.

11. You wrote, "Organic materials in the layers include algal spores, fish scales, arthropod droppings and body parts, pollen and spores of higher plants, etc. Some layers are interrupted by the remains of fish

and other vertebrates. Some layers are broken by mud-cracks and crystals of salt." I don't see this as posing a major problem for either approach discussed above.

12. You wrote, "...you have not answered my eye-witness testimony proving the existence of at least three glacial periods which commenced at the end of Noah's Flood." I responded, "We are trying to stay on task. The number of Ice Ages is another topic. Briefly, I do not have too much difficulty with Ice Ages (plural) if they follow closely one upon the other. It does not take an Ice Age to bury trees, however. An erupting Mt. St. Helens is quite adequate."

13. You wrote, "You will not commit yourself to a date for Noah's flood or say whether Ussher's date of 2348 BCE is correct or not." I responded, "Again, this is somewhat off task. Briefly, Ussher's date may be too late. Abraham lived around 2000 BC. The flood may have taken place around 4000 BC I do not have a definite date, but the date I have supplied seems reasonable to me. 3500 might be better; I don't know. I don't believe the Bible requires a specific year. Matthew 1:1 says that Jesus was "the son of David, the son of Abraham." Here we have the span of 2,000 years and only three persons are mentioned. Matthew did not intend for anyone to believe that Jesus was an immediate descendant of David or that David was an immediate descendant of Abraham. There is room for expansion."

14. You wrote, "I hope you are beginning to see that you have a serious problem here." I responded, "I

am not. In fact, I am becoming even more convinced that your varve argument is weakening. I only add in passing, because this is off topic, that you also have a very serious problem getting life from non-life without Life Himself (John 14:6) creating it."

15. You wrote, "Regardless of whether or not the GRS laminae are annual deposits or not, you have to come up with *a precise mechanism for their formation...*You must explain how three million of them could form so quickly." I covered this above.

16. Finally, I end with some questions for you. Exactly how many GRF varves are there? If the earth is 4.5 billion years old (your view), why are there so many missing varves? Eight to nine million varves is a far cry from 4.5 billion! And why was the climate so consistent in this limited area for eight to nine million years while the rest of the earth experienced drastic changes in the environment? Finally, how do you account for the massive fish burial "events" that even uniformitarians agree are unusual?

One of my creationary friends wrote on this point, "...two facts about the Green River Formation in Wyoming that challenge the notion that varves represent a year's worth of lake sediments. (1) Fossil catfish are found in excellent states of preservation over an area of 16,000 sq. kilometers of this formation. Given that dead fish placed on a muddy marsh floor and protected from scavengers by wire cages decay significantly in less than a week, such remarkable preservation hints at very rapid burial rather than slow, annual accumulation. (2) Two layers of volcanic ash within the formation, each presumably from a single event that deposited ash over a wide area, are separated by differing numbers of varves (from 1,160 to 1,568). This suggests that varve counting is not an accurate method of determining age."[120]

Conclusion

This is not meant to be a definitive explanation of the Green River varves; rather, it is an attempt to show that Christians do not have to be afraid of interpretations that supposedly disprove the Bible. Frank Zindler had/has faith in his interpretation and has chosen to disbelieve the Bible. I do not have faith in his interpretation; in fact, I believe his interpretation is wrong. I will say, however, that my correspondence with Mr. Zindler was quite civil.[121] We have corresponded a number of times since. Perhaps the God of love has or will touch him with His saving grace. I believe He has touched him already with His common grace throughout Frank's entire life.

This tile in the mosaic is quite different from others, but it is important for the reader to see that no topic escapes the sovereignty of King Jesus. He is the One, after all, who did "lay the foundation of the earth" (Heb.1:10) and "weighed the mountain in a balance, and the hills in a pair of scale" (Isa. 40:12, NASB).

Chapter 15

. . . .

IN GENERAL, THE RELIGION OF ISLAM AFFIRMS CREATION

This piece of the tile-mosaic pointing to Creator Christ is unique for this book. Christians and Orthodox Jews, affirming recent creation and the reality of Adam, may be gratified to learn that their Muslim neighbors and friends affirm the same. According to the Koran,[122] Islam's holy book, the heavens and the earth were created in six days (S.7:54).[123] Adam and many other biblical names are found in this document: Noah, Job, Satan, Abraham, Isaac, Jacob, Joseph, Moses, Pharaoh, Aaron, Sinai, David, Goliath, Solomon, Elisha, Jonah, Gabriel, Mary, John the Baptist, and Jesus.[124]

People of various faiths who believe in the sanctity of human life can appreciate the following words from the Koran: "He it is Who shapes you/ In the wombs as He pleases" (S.3:6).[125]

There are words in this book that are surprising and/or strange, however. Changing men into "apes" (S.2:65)[126] is curious, but the announcement to Mary of the "gift of a pure son"[127] is somewhat surprising. Christians believe that the Lord Jesus Christ is indeed "pure"—without sin of any kind.

People affirming biblical creation also do not find plural pronouns for deity offensive. Muslims, who are staunchly Unitarian (denying the tri-personality of God), have the word, "We," often appearing in the Koran and standing for God.[128] In the Bible, God said, "Let us make man in our image, after our likeness" (Gen. 1:26).

The fact that the Lord Jesus Christ is Creator God, however, is denied in the Koran. According to the Muslim scriptures, He, "Christ Jesus the son of Mary/ Was (no more than)/ A Messenger of Allah."[129] Additionally, we read, "They disbelieved indeed/ Those that say/ That Allah is Christ/ The son of Mary/ Say: 'Who then/ Hath the least power/ Against Allah, if His Will/ Were to destroy Christ/ The son of Mary, his mother,/ And all-every one/ That is on the earth?/ For to Allah belongeth/ The dominion....'"[130]

The Koran also denies another key teaching of the Christian faith, the crucifixion of the Lord Jesus Christ as an atonement for sin (cf. S.4:157). Some Muslims are of the opinion that the Lord Jesus was received up into heaven without dying. These two doctrines, Christ's deity and His atonement for sin on the cross, are at the core of biblical faith.

How, in Love, can Christians Respond to Muslims?

One place to start is with Scripture. The Koran does not categorically deny previous revelation. The Bible was around long before Mohammed's birth, and he undoubtedly was familiar with its teachings. The Koran gives credence to the Bible. Not only are there explicit references to both

Old and New Testament passages in the footnotes, but the following passages are found in the Koran itself:

> Let the People of the Gospel/ Judge by what Allah hath revealed/ Therein. If any do fail/ To judge by/ What Allah hath revealed,/ They are/ Those who rebel.// To thee We sent the Scripture/ In truth, confirming/ The Scripture that came/ Before it, and guarding it/ In safety: so judge/ Between them by what Allah hath revealed..." (S.5:47-48).

> If thou wert in doubt/ As to what We have revealed/ Unto thee, then ask those/ Who have been reading/ The Book from before thee:/ The Truth hath indeed come/ To thee from the Lord:/ So be in no wise/ Of those in doubt" (S.10:94).

The Title, Christ, is Applied to Jesus in the Koran

The Lord's being referred to as Christ Jesus in the Koran[131] is remarkable, for it unwittingly admits that the Lord Jesus is the promised Messiah.[132] Why was/is there not, correspondingly, a large body of literature spanning centuries prophesying the arrival of Mohammed? There was and is for Messiah Jesus. The entire Old Testament, written hundreds of years before the Lord Jesus came and by many authors, prophesied of a coming Messiah who would accomplish salvation for God's people. Moreover, some of these spoke of His death and resurrection.

Second, the Old Testament, spanning many centuries, indicates that the coming Messiah would be far more than a mere prophet. He would be the Creator, Jehovah God in human flesh:

The voice of him that crieth in the wilderness, Prepare ye the way of the JEHOVAH, make straight in the desert a highway for our God. ... O Zion, that bringest good tidings, get thee up into the high mountain; O Jerusalem, that bringest good tidings, lift up thy voice with strength; lift it up, be not afraid; say unto the cities of Judah, Behold your God! Behold, JEHOVAH GOD will come with strong hand, and his arm shall rule for him: behold, his reward is with him, and his work before him. He shall feed his flock like a shepherd: he shall gather the lambs with his arm, and carry them in his bosom, and shall gently lead those that are with young."[133]

This passage (Isa. 40:3ff, KJV) was fulfilled when John the Baptist prepared people for the Lord Jesus Christ. John was the "voice" (cf. Matt. 3:3) preparing the way for Jehovah Jesus. Verses nine through eleven of the same chapter speak of God's coming and of His tender care (like that of a shepherd) of lambs. This was perfectly fulfilled with the coming of the Lord Jesus. He claimed to be the good shepherd (John 10:11) and gathered children (lambs) into His arms and blessed them (Mark 10:16). Only four verses of this chapter have been cited, but the entire chapter, pointing to the tremendous creative power of the Messiah, is rich in exalting Creator Christ.

The author of Hebrews similarly applies the wonderfully creative acts of Jehovah God as set forth in Psalm 102:25-27 to the Lord Jesus Christ (Heb. 1:10). The connection with the Lord Jesus is made clear by reading Hebrews 1:8, "But unto the Son ...." It is an understatement to say that the Lord Jesus was and is a believer in creation. Not only is He a wonderful prophet and a believer in creation, He is Himself the Wonderful Creator. Thomas the Apostle addressed Him with, "My Lord and my God!" (John 20:28).

But the Koran also Points Unwittingly to the Cross of Creator Christ.

The following words appear in the Koran: "And remember Moses prayed/ For water for his people;/ We said: 'Strike the rock/ With thy staff.' Then gushed forth/ There from twelve springs."[134]

This passage is reminiscent of the first six verses of Exodus seventeen. The Israelites were traveling in the desert and came to Rephidim, but there was no water for them to drink. They were upset with Moses and demanded water. Moses thought they were about to stone him to death.

The Lord instructed Moses to walk on ahead of the people with some elders. He was to hold the staff he had used to strike the Nile River. Astoundingly, the Lord Jehovah then said, "Behold, I will stand before thee there upon the rock in Horeb; and thou shalt smite the rock, and there shall come water out of it, that the people may drink. And Moses did so in the sight of the elders of Israel."[135]

This solemn scene is a remarkable preview of the judgment that fell on Jehovah Jesus when He hung on Calvary's cross. The staff of judgment had previously been used to strike the waters of the Nile. Now it was to come down upon the rock. Jehovah God placed Himself on trial before Moses and the people on the rock. The Apostle Paul tells us that "that Rock was Christ" (1 Cor. 10:4 KJV). The picture of the Sovereign Lord Jesus standing before Pilate and the crowds who were demanding His crucifixion comes to mind. Jehovah Jesus, the Rock, did receive the punishment due to others on the cross. He alone gave the one and true atoning sacrifice for sin, and He offers today living water (John 4:10; 7:37 KJV). Those who receive such water are forever satisfied.

Submission

Muslims stress the importance of submitting to God, and Christians agree that such is very fitting and proper. There is a major, spiritual problem, however. Mere human attempts at submission before the Maker fall so far short of the mark. All, Muslims and Christians alike, are in a hopeless state. The Koran, as seen above, only vaguely hints at the solution.

The Bible communicates a clear message of hope. That hope involves submission, the submission of the Lord Jesus Christ who was struck on the head by a staff repeatedly (Matt. 27:30) and who then submitted to the ignominy of crucifixion. Why? So that God's righteous judgment against the heinousness of sin might be met. Creator Christ was the sacrificial Lamb who would atone for the sins of the world. Where in the Koran is there any real atonement for sin?

The story does not end on the cross, however. As the Prophet Jonah was vomited out of a whale's belly, the Greatest Prophet, the Incarnate Word, burst forth from death in triumph--conquering it. The Lord Jesus is the Glorious Victor over sin, Satan, and death. He is the only Savior.

Ishmael and Isaac

The Lord Jesus, before His incarnation, appeared as Jehovah's messenger to Hagar, Ishmael's mother.[136] He also appeared to Abraham, the father of both Ishmael and Isaac. Identified also as God Himself, this wonderful Creator eventually came to earth and proved His love to all the children of Abraham and to all peoples of the earth. He said, "And I, if I be lifted up from the earth, will draw all men unto me" (John 12:32).

May all who read these words bow in humble submission, repentance, and faith before the One who went to the cross and conquered death for people of every tribe, kingdom and tongue. May His Name be praised forever.

Application

If you would like to receive real forgiveness for sins, pray to Jehovah Jesus. Since He is God, He can hear the cries of your heart. Perhaps you could pray something like this: "Lord Jesus Christ, I believe you came to earth to die on a cross for my sins. Please come into my heart and forgive me. I have done many unworthy things, but I believe your blood alone can cleanse me. I'm glad you conquered death by becoming alive again. Please receive me as your own, and help me to live my life here on earth in a way that pleases you. I look forward to being with You forever in heaven."

Chapter 16

● ●

IF CREATION IS TRUE, WHY DOES EVIL EXIST?

S ome readers, who otherwise might be persuaded by my preceding arguments, may still be bothered by a nagging issue that persists in their minds. They may reason as follows:

1. If the Creator is all-powerful and loving, then there would be no suffering and evil.

2. Suffering and evil exists.

3. Therefore, the Creator (if he exists) is not all-powerful and loving.

This contra-positive argument may seem on the surface to have force, but the first line is fallacious. Over the years I have written devotionals for ICR's[137] *Days of Praise*. On a particular day, I directed the attention of a Haverford colleague to one I had just written. He commented later after reading it that he agreed with every word I said. This was an encouragement, but then he followed through with a sincere question about the sovereignty of God over such things as cancer, war, and the Holocaust. I said a few things on the spot but later handed him a more formal reply. What follows is similar to what I shared with him.

Why Even Bother to Answer This Question?

The Apostle Peter wrote, "But in your hearts set apart Christ as Lord. Always be prepared to give an answer to everyone who asks you to give the reason for the hope that you have. But do this with gentleness and respect, keeping a clear conscience, so that those who speak maliciously against your good behavior in Christ may be ashamed of their slander" (1 Pet. 3:15-16).

The reader may see that this is the same passage that motivated me to answer the varve question of my friendly atheist in a previous chapter. I am under an obligation to give my reasons for the hope that I have in a fair and just God.

I wrote the following words to my colleague at Haverford: "Many years ago, when we used to meet as an Upper School faculty in the board room, I spoke out against smoking in the faculty room. One of my peers represented me (in the minutes) as being adamantly opposed to smoking in the faculty room. At the time, I was on the radical fringe of what was acceptable—smoke had been billowing out into the hall and almost into my room. The irony is that now my fringe position is centrist."

I continued:

Some may have thought at the time that I was arrogant to think I knew what was best for my colleagues. The truth of the matter is that I was right, but not because I was more intelligent. I was simplistic, having seen pictures of lungs blackened by tar. I deduced (rightly) that such was harmful to the body. You may remember that I posted pictures in what was then the mailroom. There is an interesting passage in the Psalms that speaks to the matter of arrogance: "Your commands make me wiser than my enemies, for they are ever with me. I have more insight than all my teachers, for I meditate on your statutes" (Ps. 119:98-99). Note that the writer of those words had more insight, not because he was smarter, but because the Lord was and is smarter. The believer has answers because he is more familiar with God's *Answer Key*. Do cancer and war (specifically, the Holocaust) come from God's hands? I would like to answer this question in seven parts with a concluding summary.

In part one, I wrote that it's OK to ask sincere questions and added that we are creatures made in God's image. I said that God was eminently rational and that it was fitting that we ask rational questions. "'Come now, let us reason together,' says the LORD. 'Though your sins are like scarlet, they shall be as white as snow; though they are red as crimson, they shall be like wool'" (Isa. 1:18). Job asked all kinds of questions—so did the Psalmist (Ps.73) and Habakkuk: "The oracle that Habakkuk the prophet received. How long, O LORD, must I call for help, but you do not listen? Or cry out to you, 'Violence!' but you do not save? Why do you make me look at injustice? Why do you tolerate wrong? Destruction and violence are before me; there is strife, and conflict abounds. Therefore the law is paralyzed, and justice never prevails. The wicked hem in the righteous, so that justice is perverted (Hab. 1:1-4). The slain saints (cf. Rev. 6:10) asked another probing question from heaven.

In part two, I wrote that it was not OK to be "puffed up with pride." It is very important to be humble before God. Putting God on trial (and He has allowed this to happen more than once—see Exodus 17:1-6, for example) is arrogant! God resists the proud but gives grace to the humble. "Remember this, fix it in mind, take it to heart, you rebels. Remember the former things, those of long ago; I am God, and there is no other; I am God, and there is none like me. I make known the end from the beginning, from ancient times, what is still to come. I say: My purpose will stand, and I will do all that I please" (Is. 46:8-10).

Man today says that he will do all that he (man) pleases, but he will fail in his prideful efforts to usurp God's privilege.

Then, in part three, I wrote that we also should realize that our capacity to understand is very limited. Even if we were more intelligent than Adam (a thing very unlikely), our understanding is next to nothing when compared to God. But He has revealed Himself to us: "The secret things belong to the LORD our God, but the things revealed belong to us and to our children forever, that we may follow all the words of this law" (Deut. 29:29).

In part four, I encouraged my colleague to get to know God's character better. I wrote that the most important thing for us as humans is to know God intimately and lovingly. I quoted part of Jesus' prayer: "Father, I want those you have given me to be with me where I am, and to see my glory, the glory you have given me because you loved me before the creation of the world. Righteous Father, though the world does not know you, I know you, and they know that you have sent me. I have made you known to them, and will continue to make you known in order that the love you have for me may be in them and that I myself may be in them" (John 17:24-26).

Getting to know someone involves getting to know his character. God is loving, compassionate, holy, and just. When a human author (C. S. Lewis) creates an evil character (the White Witch)[138], we do not say that the author is evil for doing so. The character may be evil, but the author is not—especially if he has a good purpose that transcends temporary evil (the ultimate triumph of good over evil, for example).

The Sovereign of the universe, in order to display the wonder of His character to the cosmic (heavenly) host, created people who would fall into sin. Unlike Lewis' White Witch, however, Adam and Eve were created both real and good. They chose the evil (to disobey God). That sin has been imputed to us, their descendants. In Adam, all fall.

Two questions might arise at this point. First, is not the idea of a heavenly host fanciful—does it find biblical support? Second, who does God think He is—making the universe this way? In response to the first question, there is ample support for the heavenly host notion. I offer two passages. The first is from the book of Revelation (chapter five):

> Then I looked and heard the voice of many angels, numbering thousands upon thousands, and ten thousand times ten thousand. They encircled the throne and the living creatures and the elders. In a loud voice they sang: "Worthy is the Lamb, who was slain, to receive power and wealth and wisdom and strength and honor and glory and praise!" Then I heard every creature in heaven and on earth and under the earth and on the sea, and all that is in them, singing: "To him who sits on the throne and to the Lamb be praise and honor and glory and power, for ever and ever!" The four living creatures said, "Amen," and the elders fell down and worshiped (Rev. 5:11-14, NIV).

As to the notion of man's being on display before angels, see the first chapter of Job:

One day the angels [note: literally, the sons of God] came to present themselves before the LORD, and Satan also came with them. The LORD said to Satan, "Where have you come from?" Satan answered the LORD, "From roaming through the earth and going back and forth in it." Then the LORD said to Satan, "Have you considered my servant Job? There is no one on earth like him; he is blameless and upright, a man who fears God and shuns evil."

"Does Job fear God for nothing?" Satan replied. "Have you not put a hedge around him and his household and everything he has? You have blessed the work of his hands, so that his flocks and herds are spread throughout the land. But stretch out your hand and strike everything he has, and he will surely curse you to your face." The LORD said to Satan, "Very well, then, everything he has is in your hands, but on the man himself do not lay a finger." (Job 1:6-12a, NIV)

The second question was: Who does God think He is, making the universe this way? This is not unlike the hypothetical question the Apostle Paul entertained: "One of you will say to me: 'Then why does God still blame us? For who resists his will?' But who are you, O man, to talk back to God? Shall what is formed say to him who formed it, 'Why did you make me like this?' Does not the potter have the right to make out of the same lump of clay some pottery for noble purposes and some for common use?" (Rom. 9:19-21, NIV).

This may be something like asking, "Does not the author (Lewis) have the right to make with the same pen and ink some characters for noble purposes and some for ignoble?" The Apostle went on immediately to write:

What if God, choosing to show his wrath and make his power known, bore with great patience the objects of his wrath—prepared for destruction? What if he did this to make the riches of his glory known to the objects of his mercy, whom he prepared in advance for glory—even us, whom he also called, not only from the Jews but also from the Gentiles? As he says in Hosea: "I will call them 'my people' who are not my people; and I will call her 'my loved one' who is not my loved one" and, "It will happen that in the very place where it was said to them, 'You are not my people,' they will be called 'sons of the living God'" (Rom. 9:22-26, NIV)

In part five, I encouraged my colleague not to forget God's mercy: "Lest we be tempted at this point to sit in judgment over God, it would be good to remind ourselves that the same God who punishes evil with war and judgments also displays His character of love and mercy. It seems that both Adam and Eve, for example, who were expelled from the Garden, were rescued. He gave them garments of skin—requiring sacrifice of an animal. This typified the covering of righteousness the Lamb of God gives to those who humble their hearts before the cross. Adam and Eve accepted God's provision.

Part six asked the question, "But why cancer?" In answering, I referred to an experience I had had holding my father-in-law's hand as he passed from this life. Though he was (is) a Christian, he died of cancer. Why? Isn't God supposed to heal all our diseases? My wife, Prudence, had been healed of cancer! Why not her father?

I wrote, "First, my father-in-law did live much beyond the maximum of four years that was projected following diagnosis of the cancer. Fifteen years is much more than four. But also, it was a tremendous learning experience for him and others. He gained and expressed new appreciation, for example, for the passage in 1 Peter1:3-7 (NIV):

> Praise be to the God and Father of our Lord Jesus Christ! In his great mercy he has given us new birth into a living hope through the resurrection of Jesus Christ from the dead, and into an inheritance that can never perish, spoil or fade—kept in heaven for you, who through faith are shielded by God's power until the coming of the salvation that is ready to be revealed in the last time. In this you greatly rejoice, though now for a little while you may have had to suffer grief in all kinds of trials. These have come so that your faith—of greater worth than gold, which perishes even though refined by fire—may be proved genuine and may result in praise, glory and honor when Jesus Christ is revealed.

My father-in-law, a former executive with Firestone Tire and Rubber, would go with men from his church to the Akron City Jail and speak to some on death row. I would wheel him around in his wheelchair. When they spoke of death row, he identified with them by saying he was on death row, too. He rejoiced in the opportunity to share with them freedom in Christ."

I continued, "Cancer for my wife was a learning experience. For one thing, we learn utter dependence on God. The Lord comes very close to His children when they suffer. He never leaves them nor forsakes them. Cancer is not such a bad thing if it means closeness to the greatest Lover of all time, and death for the believer is like birth—a moving from one location to a much bigger world.

184

Part seven was entitled, "Why war and the holocaust?" I wrote, "I don't know if you have ever read my articles dealing with Hitler's evil and the resistance of Christians to it. I mention Corrie ten Boom in one of those two articles, and I lent to you a copy of the video, *The Hiding Place*, featuring her story. She is interviewed at the end. We have the notion that the ultimate evil that can come our way is physical death, but this is not right. The Lord said, "Do not be afraid of those who kill the body but cannot kill the soul. Rather, be afraid of the One who can destroy both soul and body in hell." (Matt. 10:28).

Continuing, I wrote, "Corrie's sister died in one of the prison camps. Her family's crime was trying to save Jews. The apostle Paul wrote: "Therefore we do not lose heart. Though outwardly we are wasting away, yet inwardly we are being renewed day by day. For our light and momentary troubles are achieving for us an eternal glory that far outweighs them all. So we fix our eyes not on what is seen, but on what is unseen. For what is seen is temporary, but what is unseen is eternal" (2 Cor. 4:16-18).

Death in a concentration camp, for the believer, is a "light and momentary trouble." The Apostle Peter wrote:

> To this you were called, because Christ suffered for you, leaving you an example that you should follow in his steps. He committed no sin, and no deceit was found in his mouth. When they hurled their insults at him, he did not retaliate; when he suffered, he made no threats. Instead, he entrusted himself to him who judges justly. He himself bore our sins in his body on the tree, so that we might die to sins and live for righteousness; by his wounds you have been healed. For you were like sheep going astray, but now you have returned to the Shepherd and Overseer of your souls" (1 Peter 2:21-25, NIV).

Conclusion of My Letter

I concluded as follows: "I do not profess to have answered every aspect of this question, but I find God's revelation of Himself in His Word satisfying to me. I allow that there are many dimensions beyond my ability to understand, but He has proven His goodness to me in so many ways that it would be utter folly for me to do other than to bow before Him in humble admiration, love, and praise.

If there is one passage that says it all, it might be the Apostle Paul's words in Ephesians 1:11-12 (NIV): "In Him we were also chosen, having been predestined according to the plan of Him who works out everything in conformity with the purpose of His will, in order that we, who were the first to hope in Christ, might be for the praise of His glory."

A passage in his third chapter, perhaps because it is lengthier, may actually top it, however. Paul adds:

> I became a servant of this gospel by the gift of God's grace given me through the working of His power. Although I am less than the least of all God's people, this grace was given me: to preach to the Gentiles the unsearchable riches of Christ, and to make plain to everyone the administration of this mystery, which for ages past was kept hidden in God, who created all things. His intent was that now, through the church, the manifold wisdom of God should be made known to the rulers and authorities in the heavenly realms, according to his eternal purpose which He accomplished in Christ Jesus our Lord (Eph. 3:7-11, NIV).

May the One who gives us strength to do anything—including staring in wonder at a leaf bud emerging on a flowering pear with all of its delicate complexity and filaments of fragility,[139]fill our hearts with such love and adoration of Him that we all but burst with His joy."

Epilogue

Since leaving The Haverford School, I have had continuing contact with some of my former colleagues—including the one addressed in this chapter. I am pleased that he asked the question he did because (1) many have had similar concerns and (2) it provided an opportunity for me to think through and provide an answer. Here, therefore, is a correction of the false reasoning displayed at the beginning of the chapter:

1. The Creator is all-powerful and loving.

2. Suffering and evil exists today and have existed in the past.

3. The Creator will ultimately triumph over both and display His loving and good purposes in tolerating them for a time.

One tremendous example of the above has already occurred, on Resurrection Sunday morning, when the suffering and evil of the cross gave way to life and truth and the vindication of God's suffering servant, Who came not to be served but to serve and to give His life a ransom for many.

Chapter 17

CREATION AND DEATH

There is a humorous story about a cement worker in conversation with a mother, who in turn had been admiring his work from a window just above the sidewalk. While the worker was smoothing out finishing touches on the wet surface, he was proclaiming how much he loved and valued children. The mother was impressed, but just then the school bell rang. Children came out of the school every which way, some running across his work. He started shaking his fist and cursing. Startled, the mother said, "But I thought you loved children;" to which he retorted, "I do love them in the abstract – but not in the concrete!"

As We Get Older, Death Goes from the Abstract to the Very Concrete!

In the previous chapter, we were considering evil somewhat in the abstract, but now we get more concrete. Death looms before us all. I talk now about the death of a man I never met. Fred G. Weir was drowned when a German torpedo sank the S.S. Athenia on its return voyage to Canada on September 3, 1939. This was approximately three years before I was born. At the time of impact, the liner was about 200 miles off the coast of Scotland. Fourteen hundred were on board; Mr. Weir was among the 112 who drowned. What,

This is the postcard that Fred Weir sent to my grandfather. It pictures the S. S. Athenia before it was torpedoed.

if anything, does this have to do with creation?

The Bible says, "Precious in the sight of the LORD is the death of his saints." At the time, Fred Weir was an elder of a Christian church in Goderich, Ontario. I received a letter, dated June 18, 2005, from a ninety-two year old woman whose father was the pastor of Mr. Weir's church in 1939 (when the Athenia went down). She indicated that Mr. Weir lived very near my grandfather's jewelry shop and that she for the last fifty-three years has lived in a home across from where my grandfather lived. She had high praise for Mr. Weir, who was her father's right-hand man. There is every reason to believe that Fred G. Weir was and is a saint and that he is now in the loving arms of Creator Christ.

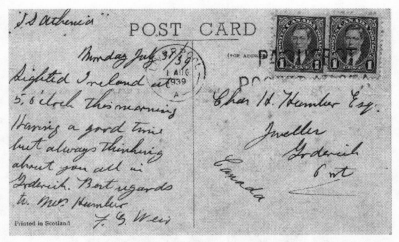

This is the back of the same card. Notice, in the last postcard this man may have ever written, the kind words this saintly man wrote to my grandfather.

Our Creator told the story[140] about a rich man who was dressed in purple and fine linen and lived in luxury every day. At his gate was laid a beggar named Lazarus, covered with sores and longing to eat what fell from the rich man's table. Even the dogs came and licked his sores. "The time came when the beggar died and the angels carried him to Abraham's side. The rich man also died and was buried."

I ask, which is better, being "buried" or "carried," to Abraham's side? Abraham was and is an Old Testament saint who had died thousands of years prior. Today, he is safe and secure in the Lord's protection. Later, the Apostle Paul wrote that for a saint to be absent from the body is to be present with the Lord![141] Additionally, Creator Christ, while on the cross, said to a nobody thief: "Today, you will be with Me in Paradise"[142] Death is very real, but so is safety in the arms of the Creator!

191

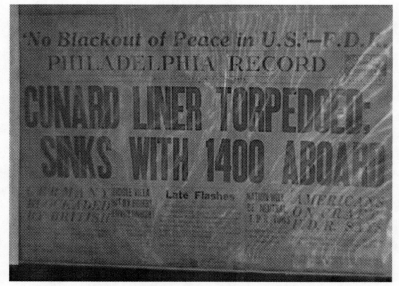

This is a newspaper that reported the disaster.

How Does This Relates to Us?

We should care about this because no one else in all history credibly claims to have overcome death. Our ultimate future, in other words, rests with our Maker, the Lord Jesus Christ. If we are linked with Him by faith, then we have tremendous hope. Our death, too, will be precious in His sight. If we are not linked with Him, then we are not linked with eternal life.

Creation?

The Lord Jesus Christ is not only the Alpha (the beginning, Creator of all); He is also the Omega (The End, the Final Purpose of all). Time (past, present, and future) belong to Him. He made us. He formed us in our mothers'

192

wombs; He keeps us alive as we ponder these words; and He is coming back to this earth. Consequently, He is more than our Creator; He is also the Recreator! He shed His blood so that people like you and me could be recreated in Him.

Application?

If you are among the recreated saints, then He is your Lord and King. You should be reading His Word daily and reaching out in love to others. Sometimes this reaching out to others involves warning friends and relatives. They may not like you for this. That is OK. Look what the world did to the best Person ever to walk this planet. They crucified Him! He said that the world will hate you.[143] "Blessed are you," He said, "when men cast insults at you, and persecute you, and say all kinds of evil against you falsely, on account of Me."[144]

If you are not yet a saint, then I would encourage you to talk to Jesus, your Creator, right now. Say something like: Jesus, be merciful to me a sinner and save me by Your blood! You see, no mere pastor or pope can get you into heaven. If your church says, "Do what we say, and we'll get you into heaven," do not believe them. The only one who can get you into heaven is Jesus. Why? Because He is the only God-man! As man, He, carrying the sins of others, was judged by the Father in human flesh. Human flesh had to suffer for human sin (the sin of Adam, our first dad).

"But," you may ask, "couldn't Jesus only save one person? How could He save millions?"

The answer is simple. Jesus can save trillions (or even quadrillions if need be) because of who He is. He is God in human flesh (the real meaning of Christmas). His blood was and is of such inestimable value to the Most Holy Father, that He, the Most Holy Son, could save even an infinite number of people. Does this mean everyone, then, will be saved? No. You must humble yourself before Jesus (repentance) and cast your life on Him for salvation (faith).

Satan would love to have torpedoed Jesus' ship. He tried to at Calvary, but that very torpedo (the cross) became the symbol of Creator Christ's victory over Satan, sin, sickness, death, and hell. May Creator Christ, Jehovah Jesus, Savior of Saints (even of those who went down with the Athenia) be praised for ever and ever!

Chapter 18

- -

A VERBAL MESSAGE ON A
PEBBLE-LIKE COIN

One of my Haverford colleagues had invited me to address a class, and on that occasion, a student asked me the question: "If God exists, why doesn't he show Himself?" On one level, the answer is easy (God revealed Himself preeminently and historically in Jesus Christ), but I think there was more to the question than that. The student, I think, was looking for something tangible and/or visible. Jesus was visible to others, but not to our eyes. Jesus was physically embraced by others, but not by us.

Some time after my father's passing, I came across a crude coin. It carries a verbal message that links in a tangible way to the historical Jesus. (I shared about this coin in assembly at the Haverford School in May of 2001, cf. photograph on back cover.) Let me give more background.

First, recall the Gospel story, how that after "Jesus was born in Bethlehem in Judea, during the time of King Herod, Magi from the east came to Jerusalem and asked, 'Where is the one who has been born king of the Jews? We saw his star in the east and have come to worship him.' When

King Herod heard this he was disturbed, and all Jerusalem with him."[145]

Why was King Herod disturbed? He was disturbed because he wanted one of his own sons to become the next king, not a divine one worthy of worship. The bronze coin pictured connects Herod's son, Archelaus, who never became king, with God's son, Jesus, Who was proclaimed King by the populous on Palm Sunday and by Pilate later the same week.

How Does the Coin Connect with Jesus and Archelaus?

The coin displayed was minted around the time the Magi asked the question of King Herod, but, according to "F. Barakat" of Barakat Antiquities & Art Gallery, it was also found on the Mount of Olives. In short, it is very likely that this very coin, found in my father's belongings, was on the Mount of Olives when Jesus rode there on a colt, speaking the words: "I tell you, if they keep quiet, the stones will cry out" (Luke 19:40).

This bronze coin was minted around the time of Jesus' birth; its Greek message relates to Archelaus.

The crowd was not quieted; nevertheless, this pebble-like coin did and still does send a message relating to the "king" question of the Magi and the praise of the Palm Sunday crown. It contains three Greek letters, ethn (EΘN)[146], an abbreviation for ethnarch (εθναρχης). Herod's son, Archelaus, never became king like his father but only attained the title, ethnarch. He did govern from 4 BC to 6 AD, but not as king. His father wanted Archelaus to become the next king, but Caesar Augustus did not ratify Herod's codicil that Archelaus should be the next king. The coin, therefore, is quietly saying something like this: Archelaus was only an ethnarch. If you want a king, look elsewhere.

Archelaus is mentioned in the Bible: "But when he heard that Archelaus was reigning in Judea in place of his father Herod, he was afraid to go there. Having been warned in a dream, he withdrew to the district of Galilee" (Matt. 2:22).

Approximately thirty years later and according to Luke, "Some of the Pharisees in the crowd said to Jesus, 'Teacher, rebuke your disciples!' Jesus' responded: 'I tell you,' he replied, 'if they keep quiet, the stones will cry out'" (Luke 10:39-40).

What exactly was it the crowds were saying? Luke explains, "When he came near the place where the road goes down the Mount of Olives, the whole crowd of disciples began joyfully to praise God in loud voices for all the miracles they had seen: 'Blessed is the King who comes in the name of the Lord'" (Lk. 19:37-38). A few days later, even "Pilate had a notice prepared and fastened to the cross. It read: JESUS OF NAZARETH, THE KING OF THE JEWS" (John 19:19). The Apostle John, who reported this of Pilate, later wrote:

I saw heaven standing open and there before me was a white horse, whose rider is called Faithful and True. With justice he judges and makes war. His eyes are like blazing fire, and on his head are many crowns. He has a name written on him that no one knows but he himself. He is dressed in a robe dipped in blood, and his name is the Word of God. The armies of heaven were following him, riding on white horses and dressed in fine linen, white and clean. Out of his mouth comes a sharp sword with which to strike down the nations. "He will rule them with an iron scepter." He treads the winepress of the fury of the wrath of God Almighty. On his robe and on his thigh he has this name written: KING OF KINGS AND LORD OF LORDS (Rev.19:11-16).

In Summary

Ethnarch Archelaus has been dead for a long time, but Handel's *Messiah* affirms today that the one who received the inscription of royalty from Pilate and the adulation of royalty from Judean residents on Palm Sunday, is indeed King of Kings and Lord of Lords. An ossuary, very possibly belonging to Jesus' brother, James, and once containing James' bones, may have been identified, but the tomb of King Jesus, according to the testimony of history, has been empty for centuries.

One of the reasons I will take this coin with me to Christian released times classes in Philadelphia (cf. Chapter Seven) is that I enjoy placing it into hands of students so that they can connect in a tangible way with the Jesus of history. I want them to know the answer to the question, "If God exists, why doesn't He show Himself?" He did, does, and will!

Chapter 19

• •

ARE DINOSAURS REALLY MILLIONS OF YEARS OLD?

Proponents of Intelligent Design focus on the feasibility of evolution and tend to sidestep the age issue (e.g. is the earth really millions of years old?). This strategy probably has some wisdom. For my part, however, I believe the scientific evidence (as well as the biblical evidence) favors a younger-earth view. It is my goal in this chapter to help the reader see that there is considerable scientific evidence for a young earth/universe.

Evolutionist Dr. Brian Richmond of George Washington University's Anthropology Department and I were in an exchange following our debate.[147] We had been answering the question, "Should public schools include only science that supports evolution or also include science that refutes evolution?" After individual presentations, we sat as panelists responding to questions from the audience. During this Q&A time, Dr. Richmond explained the process of fossilization. He said that there would no longer be any carbon or bone in dinosaur fossils. Rock mineral would replace "all the original bone." To this, I responded that one can find some dinosaur bones, supposedly sixty-five millions years old, with some collagen still remaining, adding my belief that such had been reported, and offered to send him the information.

Soft Dinosaur Tissue

More recent revelations (appearing in the March 25, 2005 issue of *SCIENCE*) seem to vindicate the creationist's position (that dinosaur bones can still have original protein) and show the evolutionary position (that dinosaur bones can have no original materials present due to their supposed millions-of years antiquity) to be flawed.

The title for this March 25, 2005 article is "Soft-Tissue Vessels and Cellular Preservation in Tyrannosaurus rex" (by Mary H. Schweitzer et al, p. 1952ff). The first sentence reads as follows: "Soft tissues are preserved within the hind-limb elements of Tyrannosaurus rex (Museum of the Rockies specimen 1125)." (See pictures on the front and back covers of this book.) The final paragraph makes the following admission: "These data indicate that exceptional morphological preservation in some dinosaurian specimens may extend to the cellular level or beyond." In online material supporting the article, the conclusion reads in part: "We have shown that soft tissue structures remain in more than one dinosaur, thus the preservation of soft tissue in dinosaur fossils may prove to be a fertile area of study." The conclusion then ends with these words: "how mineralization could result in flexible, transparent and pliable structures in multiple specimens of various phylogenetic affinities and temporal and geographical origin is not clear."

Mary Schweitzer, PhD, has connection with the Department of Marine, Earth and Atmospheric Sciences, North Carolina State University in Raleigh, North Carolina. On June 30, 2005, I wrote to her, referring to my exchange with

Dr. Richmond. I represented his position as being, "there would no longer be any carbon/bone in dinosaur fossils," adding that "Rock mineral would replace all the original bone." I told her that my position was "that one can find some dinosaur bones with collagen still remaining." I then asked, "Do you have a theory as to what the soft tissue you have discovered is? Do you think some collagen may still exist in dinosaur bones?"

"Never in my wildest dreams would I have predicted what we found."

Dr. Schweitzer graciously responded the same day writing as follows: "Hmmm. I guess that the definition of fossilization needs a bit of refining for your friend. And, a *lot* of redefinition now, on everyone's part, since our current theories do not account for soft tissue and cellular preservation ... *some* dino bone is quite high in carbon, for example. ... I have spent most of my career arguing that small epitopes (fragments of protein, often only a few amino acids in length, to which antibodies might bind) may be preserved in bone. *Never in my wildest dreams would I have predicted what we found* (emphasis added). We are spending this summer in Montana ... We are looking for collagen and other proteins, using a variety of techniques. Our data our intriguing ... I hope that there are remnants of collagen and other informative proteins present in the bones and soft tissues. That is what we are looking for. Thanks for your interest."

Please notice how cautious evolutionists are in yielding ground. *Science*, the publication in which Dr. Schweitzer's article appeared, likely does not want to vindicate or affirm a creationist's position. The language in the article is guarded. For instance, the word "may" in the second quoted statement from the article (above) is one example, and the article goes on to speculate that there may be "some kind of unknown geochemical replacement process" (p. 1955) going on, thus providing yet another last-straw out from creationary conclusions. Such caution is understandable. Creationists, too, can and perhaps should be cautious. Is it possible that soft tissue could "survive" even going back merely thousands of years (to Noah's flood)?

On August 16, 2005, Dr. Michael Behe, famed author of *Darwin's Black Box*, wrote to me: "It was very nice to speak with you too on Sunday ... I had heard about Dr. Schweitzer's work, and it is indeed unexpected and amazing."

Dr. Kurt P. Wise, a Harvard trained scientist under Stephen J. Gould, wrote the following to me: "I think protein preservation from the flood (which only occurred forty-three to forty-four thousand years ago) is a bit of a strain to organic chemistry theory; preservation from sixty-five million years ago would truly (be) mind-boggling. I therefore concur with her statement and appreciate her honesty."[148]

Dr. Richmond was less guarded, however. For example, I wrote him the following on the day after our debate: "I'm taking the liberty of attaching an article from *Science News* (October 3, 1992, p. 213) concerning protein in dinosaur bone. You seemed to be unaware of such."

Five days later, Dr. Richmond responded: "Thank you for the journalist report on claims of finding dinosaur protein. From the researchers' interviews, it is clear that it had not yet passed the rigorous scrutiny of other researchers. Now that it's been over a decade, do you know if their tentative report has been substantiated, or was it just contamination?"

Dr. Richmond, therefore, continued to be skeptical. He categorized the article as a "journalist report", speculating that it had not yet passed rigorous scrutiny and suggested further the possibility of contamination. In short, he revealed an evolutionary bias, consistent with his position in the debate, that dinosaurs sixty-five million years old cannot retain protein.

On March 25, 2005, I again wrote to Dr. Richmond asking, "Did you see this? Maybe the dino-samples are not as old as evolution assumes! Comment?" Along with this note, I sent a copy of Jeff Hecht's article, "Blood vessels recovered from T rex bone" from the *New Scientist*.

Dr. Richmond responded, "When I came to work this morning, the earth looked flat. Comment? I've attached the original scientific papers because I'm certain you wouldn't want to base your knowledge of science on layperson media reports. Enjoy, Brian"

Here is some of what I wrote in response: "Thank you for the articles. You wrote, 'When I came to work this morning, the earth looked flat. Comment?' It seems now … that the 'rigorous scrutiny' you sought, a year and a half ago, has been met. When we look at an Egyptian mummy, things are pretty disintegrated, and these mummies were 'preserved.' Multiply three thousand (approximate age of mummies) by a factor of twenty-two thousand and you get the supposed age of dinosaurs. Does it not stretch the boundaries of your credulity to imagine dinosaur tissue twenty-two thousand times as old as mummies still having flexibility? You were skeptical 1.5 years ago; are you now allowing for that kind of stretch? What does it take to have people consider that the millions/billions notion is flawed? … Cordially, Paul"

Undulating Mountains

As has been mentioned, I serve as Executive Director of Skilton House Ministries, Inc. In one of our 2004 *In the Beginning* publications, a photograph was reproduced with permission of the Minister of Public Works and Government Services, Canada, 2004, and courtesy of Natural Resources Canada, Geological Survey of Canada.[149] It is of southern Rocky Mountains near Sullivan River in British Columbia. None of us were present when the mountain range was formed, but the clear impression is given that the undulating layers were soft at one time. Hardened rock snaps, but there is a "smoothness" associated with the folds of these buckled mountains. What tremendous mechanisms, we might ask, could produce such a result? The global flood in Noah's day is a sensible answer!

Some secularists probably would scoff at such a notion, but this response is insufficient. They must offer a sensible alternative. They should also, for their own good, recognize their anti-theistic bias. They may think they are so-called neutral, but the fall of our first human parents into sin resulted in our hearts being bent away from our gracious Creator.

Preposterous?

In *Dinosaurs*, a book for children, the first sentence reads as follows: "Millions of years ago dinosaurs roamed the earth." The first sentence in the book's next paragraph mentions that dinosaurs were on earth for one hundred and twenty million years.[150] I am confident that similar statements are made in most dinosaur books for children. It is a tenet of secular faith that evolution made dinosaurs long before it made man, but secularists deny that this is indoctrination. They see it as a proven fact of science, but it is not.

Oxford's Dr. Richard Dawkins wrote, "Any science teacher who denies that the world is billions (or even millions!) of years old is teaching children a preposterous, mind-shrinking falsehood."[151] (Refer back to my interactions with Dr. Dawkins in chapter eight.)

What About the Age of Oil and Harvard's Dr. Gould?

Another of evolution's leaders was Harvard's Dr. Stephen Jay Gould. His public words, expressed in a 1982 issue of *Natural History*,[152] are very much a part of the reigning paradigm of current evolutionary thinking. They, like Dawkins' misleading transfer of numerical information, need to be challenged, however. Gould was reporting on his experience in Little Rock, Arkansas, regarding the Arkansas act that was friendly toward creation science. He (like Dr. Dawkins) was extremely intolerant of creation science, seeing it as an oxymoron. This is what he wrote:

> One witness pointed to a passage in his chemistry text that attributed great age to fossil fuels. Since the Arkansas act specifically includes "a relatively recent age of the earth" among the definitions of creation science requiring "balanced treatment," this passage would have to be changed. The witness claimed that he could not do it. Why not? retorted the assistant attorney general in his cross examination. You only need to insert a simple sentence "Some scientists, however, believe that fossil fuels

are relatively young." Then, in the most impressive statement of the entire trial, the teacher responded. I could, he argued, insert such a sentence in mechanical compliance with the act. But I cannot, as a conscientious teacher, do so. For "balanced treatment" must mean "equal dignity" and I would therefore have to justify the insertion. And this I cannot do, for I have no valid arguments that would support such a position.

Does This "Most Impressive Statement of the Entire Trial" Stand Today?

Less than a month after Judge William Overton ruled that the Arkansas act was unconstitutional, an article appeared in *The New York Times* (January 29, 1982) entitled, "Divers Find Natural 'Oil Refineries,'" by Walter Sullivan. A key statement in the article reads as follows: "Ordinarily oil has been thought to form over millions of years, whereas in this instance the process is probably occurring in thousands of years." Later, that same year, *Sci-Quest* reported: "Under the unique conditions in these environments, organic matter from dead plankton and other marine life is transformed into petroleum products in thousands, rather than millions of year...."[153]

More recently, an article appeared in *Discover* that is astounding.[154] The first sentence reads as follows: "In an industrial park in Philadelphia sits a new machine that can change almost anything into oil." Further down, one reads: "The process is designed to handle almost any waste product imaginable, including turkey offal, tires, plastic bottles, harbor-dredged muck, old computers, municipal garbage, cornstalks, paper-pulp effluent, infectious medical waste, oil-refinery residues, even biological weapons such as anthrax spores."

How long does this process take? Notice the word, "annually," in what follows: "Just converting all the US agricultural waste into oil and gas would yield the energy equivalent of four billion barrels of oil annually. In 2001 the United States imported 4.2 billion barrels of oil."

The corporate profile of the organization referred to in the article reads as follows: "Changing World Technologies, Inc. is an energy and environmental service company that provides funding and management expertise to its joint ventures and wholly owned subsidiaries. Our mission is to identify, introduce and commercialize environment-friendly energy technologies to the international marketplace. Our company's products and services are aimed at providing energy independence, ensuring a better future for industry, business, engineering and science throughout the world. CWT is the owner and developer of processes that convert industrial waste and low-value streams into fuels, oils, gases and carbons, with no hazardous emissions into the environment."[155]

There are, of course, many other scientific reasons for believing the earth is not anywhere near as old as evolutionary faith intimidatingly affirms. Here are some other reasons for the reader to consider:

Speed of Light

The speed of light can change! The *New York Times* (February 18, 1999) reported that light may be slowed by a factor of twenty million. If this is so, then why should it be thought that light could not at one time have traveled faster than it does at present—challenging the notion that it must necessarily take millions of years for light to travel over huge distances? Even secular, evolutionary scientists have theorized that the initial expansion of the universe exceeded the speed of light by many times.[156]

Einstein's General Theory of Relativity

Einstein's General Theory of Relativity may help us better understand just how light from distant stars could be seen on earth much sooner than long-age theorists proclaim. The theory says that gravity warps time so that distant clocks run faster than those on earth. This may be hard to follow, but it is based on the prevailing scientific theory and is demonstrable. The theory, in other words, may actually support a young-earth view.[157]

Radiohalos

Dr. Russell Humphreys, referenced in the endnote of the previous paragraph, has a PhD in physics. In personal correspondence, he gave me permission to share his thoughts about radiohalo evidence for a young earth. Here are excerpts:

Radiohalos are the microscopic bulls-eye sets of rings (really sections of nested spheres) that form in a crystal (usually biotite, a dark mica) around a tiny center containing radioactive nuclei. Each ring is a "scar" made in the crystal by alpha particles having a particular energy. Uranium-238 (U-238) makes a very common type of halo having eight rings, one from each alpha emission as it decays down to Lead-206. Another very common type of halo comes from the decay of Polonium (Po), one of the intermediate elements formed as U-238 decays to lead. Po halos have one, two, or three halos, depending on which isotope is decaying. But the five rings which would come from their parent nuclei are missing. Since

208

all three isotopes of Po have very short half-lives, there seems to be no *natural* way to form Po halos without forming at least some of the missing five rings as well. As part of the RATE initiative, Andrew Snelling and Mark Armitage systematically looked at many thousands of slides of biotite from dozens of geologic sites, finding and cataloging thousands of radiohalos. It is the largest such study we know of.

New findings. Andrew and Mark discovered some crucial new facts about Po halos:

(1) Their radiocenters look like *hollow bubbles*, in contrast to the solid zircon centers of Uranium halos. (2) Almost always there is a U-238 halo *within one millimeter* of a Po halo, often much closer than a mm. (3) Almost always the U-238 radiocenter is in the *exact same cleavage plane* of the mica as the Po radiocenter.

New theory. Andrew (and the rest of the RATE project) thinks that accelerated nuclear decay produced lots of daughter products in the U-238 center, particularly Radon-222 (Rn-222) and its descendants Po-218, Po-214, and Po-210. Hot water flowing along the cleavage planes of the mica would carry these daughter isotopes along with it. (The hot water comes from formation of various minerals in the cooling molten rock.) Along the way, some Radon and Polonium nuclei decay, but because they do not decay at particular locations, no spherical halos form. Then the Polonium atoms encounter a deposit of sulphides (common in biotite) and cling to it because of a chemical attraction. Now that there is a central point for the alpha particles to proceed from, a Po halo quickly forms. Heat from the decaying Po could form the small "bubble" around the sulphide deposit.

Timescale. It takes roughly one hundred million alpha particles to form a halo ring. Yet this theory places severe constraints on the time during which that amount of decay can take place. It takes a temperature difference of dozens of degrees C to drive the hot water through the mica. While the cooling mica is above 150 degrees C (the annealing temperature of mica), no halo can form. When it cools below roughly 50 degrees C, no water can flow. So the halo can form only during the time the mica is between those two temperatures. That time is short, weeks or months (not millions of years), because the flowing water carries heat efficiently, smoothing out the temperature differences that drive the flow. For the tiny amount of uranium in the U-238 radiocenter to produce hundreds of millions of Rn and Po atoms within only a few weeks demands highly accelerated nuclear decay.

Conclusion. This new theory explains all the known facts about Polonium halos very nicely, in contrast to previous theories. But it cannot work without accelerated nuclear decay.

Reference. Don DeYoung's forthcoming book for laymen on the RATE project, *Thousands, Not Billions: Challenging an Icon of Evolution*, is very well written and devotes a whole chapter to the new radiohalo evidence. Master Books is the publisher, and it should be available after November 2005 from a variety of creationist sources, including CRS books.

Carbon 14

As previously explained (Introduction), many objects, supposedly hundreds of millions of years old, date to mere thousands of years (sixty thousand years or *less*) using sophisticated ^{14}C dating methods. Put another way, whenever a once-living organism (now a fossil supposedly millions of years old) is examined, residual ^{14}C still remains, but zero should remain for fossils even sixty thousand years old![158]

Joggins, Nova Scotia, 2003

Tree Fossil Cutting Through Layers

Living Fossils

Living things like the Coelacanth fish and Wollemi pines were thought to have become extinct millions of years ago, for there was no evidence for their existence in layers thought to be intervening, but Coelacanth fish[159] and Wollemi pines still live on earth! How can organisms that supposedly became extinct still be living? At least some geological assumptions (fostering evolutionary faith), in other words, need to be challenged. Other examples of living fossils include tuatara, cockroaches, ginkgo trees, horseshoe crabs, gars (fish), sturgeons, bats, tapirs, aardvarks, platypus, magnolia trees, ferns, and alligators.

Helium content of zircons point to youthfulness; the earth's decreasing magnetic field suggests youth; experiments in sedimentology challenge accepted evolutionary thinking; continental erosion rates preclude tremendous ages; coral growth rates have been found to be more rapid than earlier thought; the receding rate of Niagara Falls points to youthfulness; polystate fossils demand a different interpretation of strata; the size of river deltas preclude long ages; earth's recorded history is thousands of years (not millions); the rate of earth's spin suggests youthfulness; craters are on the surface (not in lower layers); there are many fossil anomalies pointing to the need of reinterpreting the strata data; the receding of the moon from the earth suggests youth; the existence of comets (that they did not burn out long ago) suggests youth, etc.

There are battles to be fought in the world, such as terrorism, confused thinking, drugs, murder, disease, hatred, ego, and death. There is one, however, who is the embodiment of wisdom and knowledge (science). This life actually conquered a major problem for us—death. He is our Creator, God in human flesh. The same yesterday, today, and forever, He knows all about chronology. The first and the last Himself, He created time out of regard for our limitations.

Some scientists may presume to know more than Jehovah Jesus, but that is because they, like us, are children of rebellious parents. May all children of Adam and Eve look to this "Last Adam," the crusher of Satan's head (Gen. 3:15). He is the only source of biology and made all dinosaurs. He even referred to a dinosaur-like creature in Job 40:19 as being "the chief of the ways of God" (KJV). Small-tailed hippopotamuses do not seem to fit the description; dinosaurs with cedar-like tails do! If Jesus referred to dinosaurs, then "chief" (rex) makes sense. Moreover, Job was familiar with these creatures; in other words, they did not live millions of years before Job existed. The bones of these creatures (existing in museums) are made like bars of iron (Job 40:18; cf. front cover). Scientists try to create life, but Jesus, with no PhD, succeeded billions of times—more reasons why He is the greatest scientist of all time.

Chapter 20

. . . .

MATHEMATICAL
CREATION

Instead of talking about mathematics and placing it as a tile in the mosaic of creation (cf. Purpose Statement), let me alter the metaphor just for this chapter. Think of a long hall with many doors on either side. We have opened a number of them already on our journey, but the vista before us while opening the mathematical door is marvelous. Numbers (algebra) and objects (3-D geometry) are everywhere. God is a tri-personal unity (three in one). He knows all the functions of time, dimensions of space, and is intimately aware of every aspect of each of us (including the number of hairs on our heads). Every electron in the universe is under His control, and He works all things after the counsel of His will (Eph.1:11).

In mathematics, students will sometimes study probability. The improbability of DNA occurring naturally is staggering, and in an Associated Press article entitled, *Famous Atheist Now Believes in God* (December 9, 2004), we read the following opening words: "A British philosophy professor who has been a leading champion of atheism for more than a half-century has changed his mind. He now believes in God more or less based on scientific evidence, and says so on a video released Thursday. At age eighty-one, after decades of insisting belief is a mistake, Anthony Flew has concluded that some sort of intelligence or first cause must have created the universe. A super intelligence is the only good explanation for the origin of life and the complexity of nature, Flew said in a telephone interview from England."

Specifically, it is the complexity of the DNA that baffled him.

I personally have taught mathematics for over thirty years. At the beginning of my career, there was a symposium involving evolutionists at the Wistar Institute in Philadelphia. A 140-page report was complied, entitled, *Mathematical Challenges to the Neo-Darwinian Interpretation of Evolution.* In the report, University of Paris' Dr. Marcel Schutzenberger, a mathematician, said, "Thus, to conclude, we believe that there is a considerable gap in the neo-Darwinian theory of evolution, and we believe this gap to be of such a nature that it cannot be bridged within the current conception of biology."

Not only does mathematics challenge evolutionary theory, but Charles Darwin was himself mathematically challenged (on his own admission): "I attempted mathematics, and even went during the summer of 1828 with a private tutor ... to Barmouth; but I got on very slowly. The work was repugnant to me, chiefly from my not being able to see any meaning in the early steps of algebra."[160]

Darwin had one degree, and it was in theology. Why is this man so revered? Could it be because he provided a rational excuse to reject God and live like a party-animal?

Looking at Creation through Mathematical Eyes

In chapter five of this book, I recounted close-up encounters with the Creator. The first occurred after a trip to Maine. Let me recount mathematics I found on that trip. The general location was Moosehead Lake (central Maine), but more specifically my wife, younger son, and I were hiking to a B-52 bomber wreckage site on Elephant Mountain (near Moosehead Lake). We found two items of mathematical interest—one involving bones.

The first item could easily be mistaken for a honeycomb, but was not. I am no expert in plane construction, but I surmise that the piece (about the size of a small pancake) was either part of a wing or some support structure.

The honeycomb structure simulating God's creation.

This first item begins a wheel of ideas turning in the mind of one keen on mathematics. How many things do we see copyrighted by God but copied by man? Actually, I think the Creator enjoys seeing us copy Him.

The structure found, looking much like a honeycomb, is a series of interlocking hexagonal prisms yielding maximum support with minimum (zero) wasted space. How many other structures do we copy from God's handiwork?

Bass Crash

Concentric circles come to mind as one plops a floating lure in amongst tree stumps at the west side of Indian Pond (also near Moosehead Lake). Fishing for small-mouth bass, we could see water ripples increase in ever-widening circles until you are suddenly startled by the crash of a bass breaking the surface creating this time macro-ripples and more concentric circles.

Geometric Shapes

The orbits of comets are elliptical. Starfish and sand dollars have pentagonal shapes. The Chambered Nautilus is mathematically precise. These and other examples not mentioned suggest that mathematicians are artists who appreciate the orderliness of nature. Even the undulating line cast into the sunset near the tree stumps reminds one of trigonometric functions and continuity.

Bones?

No, these were not human (although, sadly, there were a dozen or so fatalities associated with the bomber crash in January of '63): The bones we found were much bigger.

Here the author is holding a rib bone with others above.

Peter, my son, was the first to spot them at the periphery of the crash site.

Again, I am no expert, either about plane construction or animal osteography, but my guess is that the bones were from an adult moose. We looked all over for the skull but did not find it. Our dog, Shadow, was with us. He had rolled frantically in something before we discovered the bones, but I didn't think until after we left the area that we could have checked that spot for the skull.

Symmetry and series, both mathematical concepts, come to my mind when looking at certain of the bones we found. Connected, they were congruent and apparently related to the vertebrae system in some way. A rather lengthy bone extends down (or up, depending on orientation) from each. This seemed peculiar to me. Unless I was mistaken, rib bones should extend symmetrically from either side of vertebrae, but these extended bones coincide with an axis of vertebra symmetry. We also kept a rib and a leg bone.

This find can start similar wheels of ideas turning in mathematical minds. An opening in the center of each vertebra is elliptical and suggests a cylinder. How many of our body parts are symmetrical? When we speak of series and symmetry in mathematics, are we not copying ideas originating elsewhere? It was Johann Kepler, the founder of physical astronomy, who said that he was "thinking God's thoughts after Him." More recently, Francis Collins, Director of the National Human Genome Research Institute, is quoted in the August 15, 1997 issue of *Science*: "When something new is revealed about the human genome, I experience a feeling of awe at the realization that humanity now knows something only God knew before."

Maine is a beautiful place to visit. Of course, there is mathematics all around us (in every state), but the two props mentioned (generating related mathematical thinking) were of special interest.

Fractions?

Many can relate to Darwin's frustration with mathematics, but mathematics bears testimony to the integrity, beauty, orderliness, and wonder of Creator Christ.

Take the number, π. Where did it come from? Why would any mathematician in his right mind invent it? Well, the answer is that it was not invented. Take any circle in the universe, measure its circumference (distance around), divide by its diameter (distance across through the center), and you always get π.

Someone could ask, "You mean it does not make any difference how big or small the circle, this ratio (fraction) is always the same?" Yes. Note the integrity and trustworthiness of the creation we live in and enjoy. Mathematical relationships are part of God's thinking. We do not invent them; we discover them.

Many adults detest simple fractions. Adding 1/2 and 1/3, for example, is a challenge, but it is partly because they have never really appreciated the beauty of unity (1). This number is the only one in the universe that has the property that when you multiply it with another, you do not change the value. Multiply your age by 1; you did not change. Multiply your bank account by any other number besides 1; you will change the amount of money you have in that account. By multiplying each fraction, 1/2 and 1/3, therefore, by different forms of unity (1), you may obtain a common denominator and add the fractions.[161]

As intimated above, mathematics can be divided into two major categories—algebra (numbers) and geometry (points). The number line is a combination of these two concepts. A line is a set of points (geometry); the coordinates of these points are sets of numbers (algebra).

In a plane, you may draw a circle (geometry) and write the equation of the circle (algebra). It is remarkable that there is an equation for every point (and circle) in the plane. Every line (geometry) also has an equation (algebra). We can even think of every point in space as having coordinates.

A police officer coming upon the scene of an accident does not merely rely on the testimony of eyewitnesses. He also measures the skid marks on the road to determine how fast the car was traveling, using a mathematical speeding formula.

Doctors, compiling statistics from case studies, can make reasonable judgments about optimal amounts of medicine to give patients. Mathematics, in other words, takes some of the guessing out of prescribing. It can also help one see that gambling (e.g. playing the lottery) is a bad bet.

Cosmos *Not* Chaos

There is so much pressure placed on people to believe that we live in a capricious (chaotic) universe, but this is misleading. When three lines in a plane come together at a single point, we say that the lines are concurrent. It is typical that two lines in a plane will intersect somewhere, but that a third should go through the exact same point as the other two is very special. Consider the following facts:

1. For *every triangle in the universe*, the perpendicular bisectors of the three sides are concurrent at a single point!

2. For *every triangle in the universe*, the medians (segments from vertices to midpoints of opposite sides) are concurrent at a single point!

3. For *every triangle in the universe*, the three altitudes are concurrent at a single point!

4. For *every triangle in the universe*, the angle bisectors are concurrent at a single point!

Like π and the circle discussion (above), these features of triangles point us to a remarkable orderliness (cosmos) in the universe. We do not live in a chaotic world. Human conduct may be capricious, to be sure, but there is integrity in so many places elsewhere.

Isaac Newton

In his celebrated *Principia Mathematica*, Newton, perhaps the greatest of modern scientists wrote of the "Lord over all" and added: "He is eternal and infinite, omnipotent and omniscient; that is, his duration reaches from eternity to eternity; his presence from infinity to infinity; he governs all things, and knows all things that are or can be done."[162]

Johann Kepler

The founder of physical astronomy, Johann Kepler, was also expressive: "Great is our Lord and great His virtue and of His wisdom there is no number: praise Him, ye heavens, praise Him, ye sun, moon, and planets, use every sense for perceiving, every tongue for declaring your Creator. ...and thou my soul, praise the Lord thy Creator, as long as I shall be: for out of Him and through Him and in Him are all things.... To Him be praise, honor, and glory, world without end."

Conclusion

Evolution worships the notions of randomness and purposelessness, but mathematics is one area among many that points us to orderliness and purpose. The stranglehold grip evolution has on our educational system should be removed, for there is no rational reason to hold on to it and many reasons to reject the hypothesis outright. I hope that the reader is beginning to see that the overall mosaic of this book is pointing more and more to Creator Christ!

Chapter 21

EVOLUTIONARY HYPOCRISY?

I have already discussed, in previous chapters, differences I have had with evolutionary scientists. Dr. Dawkins, however, eventually admitted that the number he provided for the creationist side, "15," was very likely wrong. Dr. Richmond is not yet convinced that dinosaur bones can retain protein. The conflict contemplated in this chapter, however, seems potentially to involve hypocrisy.

I invited a professor of anthropology at the University of Pennsylvania to participate in a creation vs. evolution debate.[163] As we were about to have lunch together, I reminded him of a previous request, that I would like to have or purchase a less expensive, maybe even damaged, model of a Neanderthal skull. He graciously gave me one then and there. When I sought, during lunch, more details about the model, he wrote the following on a sheet of paper: "Reconstructed Skull of the Neandertal from: La Chapelle-aux-Saints (SW France)."

Six months after this lunch engagement, I had the opportunity to visit the Musee de l'Homme in Paris. I was not able to see the original skull, but I did purchase a postcard

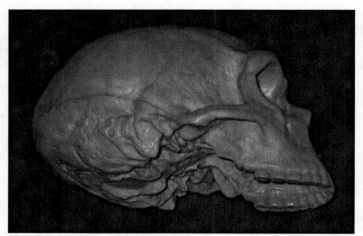

This is the skull model of La Chapelle aux Saints given to the author by the evolutionist. Notice the full line of upper teeth.

showing the right side of the Chapelle Skull. The teeth of the model seemed significantly different. There is only one upper tooth remaining in the original. It is a bicuspid with three facets on the edge. Below is a picture of the one remaining upper tooth in the La Chapelle aux Saints Skull. The chips or file-marks can be seen on the tooth.[164]

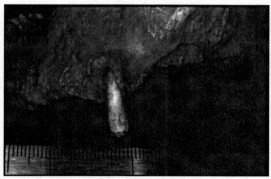

This picture of the original (courtesy of Dr. Jack Cuozzo) shows only one tooth left in the upper jaw of the La Chapelle aux Saints skull.

The reconstructed model which I had been given suggested that sixteen upper teeth would be part of the original, but this is not the case. Should not a reconstruction more closely approximate the original? The model I received, as far as the upper jaw was and is concerned, is quite unlike the original. The one upper tooth that exists in the original does not appear to be adequately represented in the model. There are no file marks. It is not set off by itself in any special way. In fact, it is confused with the other surrounding (nonexistent) teeth. Some might label such alterations and additions with anthropological license. I myself probably would not have bothered much about such imperfections had I not received significant criticism from the professor about his debating opponent after the debate and relating to yet another Neanderthal skull.

The same professor, though permitting the debate to be videotaped, does not want copies of it to be sold (or even distributed) because his opponent, Dr. Jack Cuozzo, offered evidence that the professor disputes. Dr. Cuozzo claimed that he had found a missing piece of the famous Swanscombe (Neanderthal) Skull and was for the first time, at the debate, announcing it publicly. He claimed that the mastoid piece (near the temple) fits a model of the Swanscombe Skull nicely and that there were possible trephination (surgical) marks on the fossil. This, he indicated, suggested that Neanderthals were much more advanced in medicine than evolutionists believe.[165]

As both moderator of the debate and as president[166] of the organization sponsoring it (Skilton House Ministries), I sensed a responsibility to try to resolve this impasse. On the one hand, it seemed that one debater was trying to censor the other, while on the other hand, Skilton House Ministries itself does not want to be involved in promoting falsehood. As Dr. Cuozzo's piece had been submitted to the British Museum, I contacted Professor Chris Stringer, Head of Human Origins, Department of Paleontology, The Natural History Museum, London. He wrote to me a number of times during the summer and fall following the spring debate.[167]

Dr. Stringer wrote regarding Dr. Cuozzo's artifact from Swanscombe as follows: "It is of course possible that there are, say, Mesozoic fossils in the Swanscombe gravels." (Earlier he had indicated that the artifact was only gravel, but subsequently Dr. Cuozzo pointed to evidence that the piece was true fossil.) Previously, Dr. Stringer had written: "I do consider that Dr. Cuozzo acted in good faith in this case, and did the right thing in returning this material for examination. The pieces in question, particularly the mastoid, were suggestive of human bones in their shape, although I think he would not have considered them to be fossil human bone if he had been able to make direct comparisons of their appearance with genuine fossil bone from Swanscombe."

Dr. Cuozzo, to use Dr. Stringer's words, "acted in good faith" by submitting the samples to the proper authorities for examination. There remains dispute as to whether Dr. Cuozzo's piece is from the Swanscombe Skull, but is this really just cause for tapes of the debate to be censored? Do not debates, by their very nature, necessarily involve dispute? As a creationist, Dr. Cuozzo undoubtedly discounts much of what his opponent had to say, but he was not attempting to censor a videotape involving his evolutionary opponent's views.

In the end, it may be very difficult to prove one way or the other what the actual truth is concerning Dr. Cuozzo's artifact. I personally do not know. There are arguments on both sides, but to censor the distribution of a videotaped debate because one party believes the other is not accurate seems like censorship. One could well argue from this type of reasoning that most debates should be censored. This seems somewhat like nit-picking or straining at gnats. I believe in truth and so am happy and willing to hear what an opponent has to say, but I do have difficulty reconciling the criticism of Dr. Cuozzo while at the same time passing off as reconstructions deliberately altered models of the Chapelle aux Saints Skull. Reconstructions should have as a goal to attempt as close an approximation to the original as is reasonable and possible.

Was/is hypocrisy involved? I am not the judge; however, I did write the following to the professor: "Regarding the matter of honesty, when I visited the Musee de l'Homme this past summer, I purchased a postcard of La Chapelle aux Saints. In the model you gave me, there are sixteen teeth in the upper jaw. The postcard, however, reveals no such number. You told me over lunch that the model you gave me was of La Chapelle aux Saints, but I don't believe you informed me that ... the teeth were added. Don't you think that giving a deliberately altered model is a bit misleading?"[168]

I have not received a response to these words, and I had received many previous responses. I hold open the possibility that this professor may be a little embarrassed by the inconsistency of distributing and possibly selling misleading models of the La Chapelle Skull while at the same time disallowing the sale and distribution of a videotape containing a claim by Dr. Cuozzo he disputes.

There are many other examples of evolutionary hypocrisy, events I have personally experienced and/or witnessed, such as the censorship of creation advocates, failing to own up to published fraud, refusal to admit racial bias, etc. Because we are all sinners, each of us tends to be hypocritical in one way or another—including creationists. There is only one solution to our hypocrisy. Many believers have repented of sin, some perhaps with tears. Others who have never done this might like to reflect further on this suggested prayer: Lord Jesus, I'm a proud person. I've taken pride in my learning and have all too often pushed aside the many proofs of Your skill in producing intricate beauty. At least occasionally, I have been a hypocrite. I've ignored and even hated You. I've refused to bow my proud heart before You, but I also consider that You have been long-suffering and patient toward me. You have favored me with many blessings. You even went to the cross for sinners like me. Please forgive me for my pride. Even Moses showed that bloody sacrifices were necessary for atonement. You, my Maker, came to this earth to be the Lamb of God Who takes away the sin of the world. Blood flowed from Your body when you hung on Calvary. I've never before yielded to the truth that You died and rose again for sinners. If I am indeed spiritually blind, please help me to see my blindness. If You really are the promised Messiah of God, come into my heart now and be my Savior. Thank You, Father, for sending Your only Son. In Jesus' precious name I ask this. Amen.

Chapter 22

. . . .

INHERIT THE WIND— EVOLUTIONARY PROPAGANDA

The hypocrisy displayed in this chapter is more blatant than the previous. *Inherit the Wind* is a fictionalized version of the Scopes Trial of 1925 disclaimers to the contrary. Liberals who squirm under the pressure of biblical morality seem to find solace in this bashing of Bible-believers.

The sad thing is that the play grossly misrepresents the historical personage, William Jennings Bryan. The fact that "Brady" is Bryan finds support in a personal letter written by Kirk Douglas to me. (Kirk Douglas played the part of Brady in the AT&T production of *Inherit the Wind* aired on national television more than once.) Douglas wrote. "To add to your argument, I might also include the fact that William Jennings Bryan said that he would be willing to pay the fine imposed on the young man." The fictionalized version, however, portrays a vindictive person: "Brady. (Thundering.) Your Honor, the prosecution takes exception! Where the issues are so titanic, the coon must mete out more drastic punishment...to make an example of this transgressor! To show the world."

Douglas continued. "I might also say that Bryan did read 'Darwin's Theory of Evolution' (sic). The opposite point of view was expressed in our movie for dramatic purposes."

This last sentence of Douglas is sad. Harvard's Stephen Jay Gould, in an article entitled "William Jennings Bryan's Last Campaign" (*Natural History*, November, 1987), credited Bryan for fighting against a legitimate concern and quoted Bryan: "I learned that it was Darwinism that was at the basis of that damnable doctrine that might makes right that had spread over Germany" (p. 22). Gould would not himself want to blame Darwin, but he was affirming Bryan's concern.

A lot of white supremacy jargon and implied action were floating around in the 20's, and Bryan was fighting it. Eugenicist Henry Fairfield Osborn, for example (featured by *The New York Times* in opposing Bryan, July 12, 1925) wrote in a book dedicated to John T. Scopes, "The ethical principle inherent in evolution is that only the best has a right to survive."[169] Hitler himself could just as well have said these words.

In *The New York Times* article referred to, entitled "Osborn States the Case for Evolution," Osborn cites the Piltdown race as evidence for evolution, but we now know that The Piltdown man was a hoax.

Here is the text of the letter I sent to Kirk Douglas:

Several months ago, you had an article published (I believe it was in *Parade Magazine*) entitled, "Let's Leave Make-Believe at the Movies." In it you spoke of a quiet inner awareness that says there must be a higher power responsible for the perfection of the universe we live in and that we're doing so much to destroy.

232

Most of us also sense that there is such a thing as fairness. You and I both know that your role as Matthew Brady was meant to parallel closely William Jennings Bryan. In this case, it's hard to view *Inherit the Wind* as pure make-believe. Was it really fair to Bryan to characterize him as viewing sex as sin, even original sin? I believe there is no reference to sex whatever in the actual trial, and the Christian church, represented in some measure by Bryan, believes original sin to be disobedience, not God-created sex between husband and wife. This latter is actually a gift from God. I'm concerned that both Bryan and the Christianity he represented (have) been unfairly tarnished by the *Inherit the Wind* production. Now don't get me wrong. I'm not trying to blast you, but I would like, perhaps even as a friend, to encourage you to see things from a different perspective.

Another example might be helpful. The where-did-Cain-get-his-wife issue seems also to be a red herring. Consider Genesis 5:4 where it is clear that our first parents had "sons and daughters." This is made explicit, and it is obvious that Cain married a sister. This would have had to be true even in an evolutionary setting, assuming that the evolving of humans was not a common occurrence. The business about 9 a.m. on October 23, 4004, (BC) is also misleading. Bryan made it explicit during the trial that he did not know how old the earth was.[170]

Stephen Jay Gould of Harvard, in an article entitled, "William Jennings Bryan's Last Campaign" (*Natural History*, November, 1987), affirms that "Bryan ... had correctly identified a problem!" (cf. p. 26). Bryan was aware that evolution was being used to justify German supremacy and various social evils. I'm attaching an article I wrote showing the poisoning effect it had on Stalin. The same God that has touched our "inner awareness" (as you put it) also holds us responsible for the way we represent or misrepresent our fellow human beings. He does not want us to bear false witness against our neighbor even if he has passed on to the next life.

If you agree with some of these concerns, perhaps you would be willing to respond. For example, is it not very important to remind the public and even to stress that looking at *Inherit the Wind* can be misleading about the facts of the actual trial? If you agree with me in this, would you be willing to let me quote you in an article I might write?

Our Creator is very loving and forgiving. He forgives me because of what His Son did two thousand years ago on a cross. I don't know if you have experienced the same love and forgiveness, but I know it's available to all who come to Him in humility and faith. Many great men, including William Jennings Bryan, have done this to their eternal joy. I hope you get to meet him in heaven.

Hoping to hear from you. . . .

Sincerely, Paul G. Humber

Kirk Douglas did respond, apparently agreeing in some measure with my concerns. He even added arguments I had not mentioned and did not discourage me from quoting him. Since his performance was public and he freely submitted a letter, even after I had indicated a desire to quote him, I am taking the liberty of sharing the contents of the document sent to me. It is possible that even he valued an opportunity to set the record straight. My personal view is that the producers carry greater responsibility for foisting untruths on others in the guise of quasi-history, besmirching Christianity in the process.

Here is Kirk Douglas' Response:

KIRK DOUGLAS

April 6, 1988

Dear Mr. Humber:

Thank you for your interesting letter. To answer it fully would take too much of your time and mine.

I appreciate the points you brought up, but you must keep in mind that "INHERIT THE WIND" was a fictionalized version of the Scopes trial. As a matter of fact, we brought into our film much more of the actual trial than existed in the play. But remember, the characters are never called "Bryan" or "Darrow."

To add to your argument, I might also include the fact that William Jennings Bryan said that he would be willing to pay the fine imposed on the young man. I might also say that Bryan did read "Darwin's Theory Of Evolution." The opposite point of view was expressed in our movie for dramatic purposes. On the other hand, Bryan was a fat, gluttonous person. I chose not to portray him that way.

I am happy that you were interested enough in the film to write your letter. For that, I thank you.

Sincerely,

KD:km

Mr. Paul G. Humber
327 Green Lane
Philadelphia, Pennsylvania 19128

This is a copy of Kirk Douglas' letter.

Analysis

I'm not quite sure how Mr. Douglas was able to judge the former presidential aspirant as gluttonous. The impression that I get from pictures is that Bryan was not fat. He was healthy looking and not thin; he may have been somewhat overweight. I hope this was not the basis for judging him gluttonous, however.

Perhaps the saddest part of Mr. Douglas's letter is the phrase, "The opposite point of view was expressed in our movie for dramatic purposes." Shame on AT&T for foisting misrepresentations on the public! Is this not a deliberate example of running down Bible-believing Christians? True, as Mr. Douglas stressed, the production was of a fictional character. However, Kirk Douglas himself, perhaps inadvertently, admitted (in his third paragraph about the historical Bryan), that he was portraying him. The antecedent was and is Bryan not Brady!

Presumably, millions across the nation witnessed this dramatization. Untruths, however, need to be exposed for what they are! Some producers apparently care more for money and attention than truth, but we must protest falsehood. Americans who see deception as a freedom, apparently do not know what real freedom is.

Proverbs 11:29a reads, "He that troubleth his own house shall inherit the wind." What may be in view here is one in some position of authority who withholds proper nourishment and pleasures from those under his care (family or servants). That person shall "inherit the wind." He will be pushed further and further back, away from any position of authority or influence. Those in charge of television and television productions are in positions of influence. They have responsibilities to be fair and honest in their dealings with people.

Far better it would be for media persons if they would emphasize what is honest and true. They should attend to another portion of Scripture: "Finally, brethren, whatever things are true, whatever things are noble, whatever things are just, whatever things are pure, whatever things are lovely, whatever things are of good report, if there is any virtue and if there is anything praiseworthy; meditate on these things" (Phil. 4:8).

Chapter 23

. . . .

HUMANISM'S FAITH IN EVOLUTION

W hen men, in the name of humanism, place limited mental capacities on the throne as ultimate
interpreter of reality, they should not be allowed
by public servants at the same time to foist that system of
secular religion onto the impressionable minds of public
school children—especially if all other religious systems
are excluded. But, have educators been allowed by public
servants to do this? I believe so.

For some time, I taught under Dr. Allan A. Glatthorn,
former principal of Abington High School and a friend, who
subsequently became the chairman of the Educational Leadership Division of the University of Pennsylvania's Graduate
School of Education. I believe I received from him a copy
of a paper he wrote entitled, *The New Humanities in the
Schools*. This paper used religious language. For example,
he wrote, "And finally we need an article which gives the
new humanities the blessing of *the trinity*: St. Jerome Bruner,
St. Benjamin Bloom, and St. Jean Piaget" (emphasis added).
A few pages later, he shared this poem:

Eden is gone
Since man destroyed it;
If sin you must,
Be sure you've enjoyed it.

Further on, he added:

This then is the vision I have of the total man who will be strong enough to build a better world. And it is the schools who-must produce him. Almost by default, it is our task alone. The family as we know it has lost its influence, and the church as an institution is dead. These statements are not cries of alarm designed only to shock. They are intended to be an objective report of the reality of the 1970's. The family is a group of individuals in the same house and the church serves only the hypocritical and the frightened. Only the schools remain where the new humanism can develop, a new humanism to produce the total man of the '70s. This must be our basic concern—educating the total man. In the past we educated for the religious man, or the scholarly man, or the vocational man, or the patriotic man or the social man. But now, if we are to survive, we must educate for the total man through an integrating humanism.

Let me try to sum up what I have tried to say…. In this time of crisis we are called upon as educators to act the man to commit ourselves to that task which only we can do … we are summoned to help the immature boy become the total man, to pick up the pieces, to build a better world. And it will be humanizing curriculum in an open school, led by a principal-humanist that will begin slowly but surely, to roll back the darkness that even now envelops us. For surely as man has brought about his own calamities, he can work for his own salvation. And that salvation will come through a new humanism for a new age.

The language of evolution is used above ("if we are to survive") and elsewhere in Dr. Glatthorn's paper: "he will see truth as evolving, not as something immutably fixed" and God is "always evolving as man's knowledge of Him changes." Dr. Glatthorn sought an "open" school—open to the evolving religion of humanism but closed to the changeless religion of the real Trinity.

But am I really being fair to humanism? Isn't it really non-religious? Absolutely not! Read the article, "Federal Court Finds Secular Humanism a Religion," in *Education Week*, February 11, 1987, p.1ff. It is not only a religion, but it is a religion that is hostile to Christianity. Read the *Humanist Manifesto II*. It rejects Christianity and the notion of life beyond death. It affirms faith in evolution and uses the terminology of faith explicitly.

According to "ardent evolutionist" Professor Michael Ruse (University of Guelph), evolution itself has become a religion. He wrote: "Evolution is promoted by its practitioners as more than mere science. Evolution is promulgated as an ideology, a secular religion, a full-fledged alternative to Christianity, with meaning and morality. I am an ardent evolutionist and an ex-Christian, but I must admit that in this one complaint ... the literalists are absolutely right. Evolution is a religion. This was true of evolution in the beginning, and it is true of evolution still today."[171]

Conclusion

It is academically outrageous that many educators in America are paid by our taxes to preach the godless religion of humanism to our children on campus while at the same time seeking to interfere with Christian released time which is legal, off campus, and parent approved (cf. Chapter Seven). This is horrendous hypocrisy. When will America

241

wake up? Education is never neutral. When theism was kicked out, secular humanism (atheism) filtered in.

Conclusion

"OUT OF FOCUS" EVOLUTION — GETTING CLOSER!

D r. Loren Eiseley, quoted in chapter thirteen of this book, was an evolutionary biologist who eventually became the Benjamin Franklin Professor of Anthropology and the History of Science at the University of Pennsylvania. His book, *All The Strange Hours*, is autobiographical and was published in 1975.

Here is a picture of Dr. Eiseley leaning against a "duck" made of wood.

In the book, he recounted an experience he had had with an associate, Frank Speck. They were "strolling in the Philadelphia Zoo and "came upon a wood duck paddling quietly in a little pond." His associate, impressed apparently by these "most beautifully patterned" birds, asked, "Loren, tell me honestly. Do you believe unaided natural selection produced that pattern? Do you believe it has that much significance to the bird's survival?"

In the book, Dr. Eiseley confessed that he too, at that moment, had had a similar questioning thought. Finally, he admitted in response:

> I have always had a doubt every time I came out of a laboratory, even every time I have had occasion to look inside a dead human being on a slab. I don't doubt that duck was once something else, just as you and I have sprung from something older and more primitive.... It isn't that which troubles me. It's the method, the way. Sometimes it seems very clear, and I satisfy myself in modern genetic terms. Then, as perhaps with your duck, something seems to go out of focus, as though we are trying too hard, trying, it would seem, to believe the unbelievable.

Could it be that the going "out of focus" that Dr. Eiseley referred to came from his Maker? Was the Lord in love reminding Dr. Eiseley of his own creatureliness? Sadly, it seems Dr. Eiseley did not go far with this nudge, for he continued: "I am an evolutionist. I believe my great backyard Sphexes [wasps] have evolved like other creatures. But watching them in the October light as one circles my head in curiosity. I can only repeat my dictum softly: in the world there is nothing, to explain the world; nothing to explain the necessity of life, nothing to explain the hunger of the elements to become life, nothing to explain why the stolid realm of rock and soil and mineral should diversify itself into beauty, terror, and uncertainty."

Respectfully, Dr. Eiseley was wrong because there is something in the world that explains these mysteries--a divine book. Also, exactly where did Dr. Eiseley get his dictum of denial? Does science give dictums?

Not far from the cemetery where Dr. Eiseley's remains are buried is The Haverford School, where I taught for twenty-four years. My last official act at that school was giving the 117th commencement invocation on June 8, 2001. The words I used on that occasion were much more hopeful than Dr. Eiseley's dictum:

Father in heaven, hallowed be Your name.
Thank you for rain, for fruitful seasons,
And for satisfying our hearts with gladness.

Thank you for the sun, moon, and stars.
Thank you for the bounty and freedoms
You provide for us in this nation.

You also bless us with children.
Today, we reflect especially on this – on sons You have given.
Thank you for the preciousness of their lives
When we first held them in our arms.

Thank you also for healing them and us –
and for health that You have provided over the years.

These sons have grown to be young men,
And they live in a fallen world.
There is sickness, suffering, and death.
Help them to look to You for direction.
Give them humility in the face of success,
And help them to know the path of Truth.

Open their eyes to those in need both locally and globally.
Grant them compassion and generosity.
May they walk in service and love for others.

Father, touch each heart present today with reminders of
Your grace.
May this be a worthy beginning not only for the graduates,
But for all of us.
In Jesus' name,
Amen.

Appendix 1

....

AUTOBIOGRAPHY

I began in mid-October of 1941 but was not born until nine months later (July 13, 1942).[172] My family of six (four children, including my twin sister[173]) moved from the Toronto area (Ontario) to Boston in 1945. My schooling, however, began in Canada (1947). We had returned to Canada for a summer vacation that extended into the fall. I, with blonde and curly hair, began kindergarten in a one-room school house in Selkirk, Ontario.[174]

In Boston, I continued my education at the Edward Southworth School (K-3). This school was adjacent to Mather School, America's oldest elementary school. I then attended Mather, eventually moving on (grade seven) to Boston Latin School.[175] Our family lived at 1145 Dorchester Ave., now a parking lot.

Something very vital happened to me during my formative years. The Lord of heaven had been working in my heart in various ways prior to January 17, 1950, but on that evening, I heard a sermon about Noah, his ark, and God's judgment.[176] I did not understand much surrounding the doctrine of salvation, but I knew I wanted to get right with

God. I testify now, many years later, that the Lord has kept me in His care throughout many challenges (interactions with professors at the University of Pennsylvania, teaching opportunities at Abington High School, The Haverford School, the University of Phoenix, and in debate). I have interacted with atheists, professional evolutionists, and scientists, and have found the Bible to be true and adequate. By way of contrast, I have found humanistic systems of thought to be woefully lacking. However imperfectly I have lived my life, the Lord Jesus has been, is, and will be for eternity my only Savior, Maker, Lord, and King.

I moved to Philadelphia with my parents in 1955 and attended eighth and ninth grades at Sayre Junior High School, with my twin, Priscilla. She and I were baptized at the age of fourteen by our father, Dr. Charles M. Humber. Subsequently, I attended John Bartram High School. My twin and I were part of the Block Roster.[177]

At the University of Pennsylvania, I was active in Inter-Varsity Christian Fellowship (serving as vice-president) and in track and field (pole vault/javelin). After graduating in 1964, I stayed on at Penn (working for a master's degree). Prudence and I got married in 1966, the year she graduated from Penn. I taught mathematics for four years at Abington High School[178] and served as Sunday School Superintendent of New Greenwich Light Baptist Church in South Philadelphia. With the blessing and encouragement of Abington colleagues, I left teaching to attend Westminster Theological Seminary (from 1969 to 1972). These years in seminary were very enriching ones for me.

Soon after graduating, I became the pastor of a struggling Baptist church in Whitemarsh Township (1972).[179] My starting salary was $50 per week, and I served for eight years. Twins, Paul and Ruth, were born to my wife and me on July 17, 1973. These two are now married, and my wife and I have nine grandchildren.[180]

While still serving the small church, I accepted a teaching position at The Haverford School in 1977. In 1981, my eight years of ministry with the church ended, but I continued teaching at The Haverford School. I also became the first president of Skilton House Ministries. Dr. John Skilton was a Professor of New Testament at Westminster Theological Seminary and had preached at my ordination service many years prior. While teaching and coaching at Haverford, I started writing for the Institute for Creation Research of California.

My young family and I moved in 1981 to 327 Green Lane, Philadelphia, and my aging parents joined us six months later. Peter Seth (third child) arrived in 1985. My father passed on to be with the Lord in 1988, but my mother at ninety-seven years continues to live and enjoy earthly life with us.

For two years, I served on the faculty of the University of Phoenix (Philadelphia Campus) and currently serve as the Executive Director of Skilton House Ministries, Inc. One major emphasis of this Christian ministry is promoting Christian released time education in Philadelphia's many public schools. Another emphasis is Operation Brotherhood, working with neighborhood churches to help feed needy families at Thanksgiving time.

Prudence, my wife and a nurse, serves as the Executive Director of Alpha Pregnancy Services, a pro-life ministry in center city Philadelphia where clothing and caring for hurting mothers and their rescued babies is a ministry of joy. Together, we have traveled to Africa, Antigua, and Alaska. The life verse referenced in our wedding bands is "They that wait upon the LORD shall renew their strength; they shall mount up with wings as eagles; they shall run and not be weary; they shall walk and not faint" (Isa. 40:31). He has been ever faithful to us, and our cups overflow. This does not mean we have never experienced trials. We have, but the Lord has kept us through every one. May His name be praised.

Appendix 2

HITLER'S EVOLUTIONARY
WORDS IN CONTEXT

Just as Nature does not concentrate her greatest attention in *preserving* what exists, but in breeding offspring to carry on the species, likewise, in human life, it is less important artificially to alleviate existing evil, which, in view of human nature, is ninety-nine per cent impossible, than to ensure from the start healthier channels for a future *development*.

The precondition for this does not lie in associating superior and inferior, but in the total victory of the former. The stronger must dominate and not blend with the weaker, thus sacrificing his own greatness. Only the born weakling can view this as cruel, but he after all is only a weak and limited man; for if this law did not prevail, any conceivable *higher development* (Hoherentwicklung) of organic living beings would be unthinkable.

If the process were different, all further and *higher development* would cease and the opposite would occur. For, since the inferior always predominates numerically over the best, if both had the same possibility of preserving life and propagating, the inferior would multiply so much more rapidly that in the end the best would inevitably be driven into the background, unless a correction of this state of affairs were undertaken. *Nature* does just this by subjecting the weaker part to such severe living conditions that by them alone the number is limited, and by not permitting the remainder to increase promiscuously, but making a new and ruthless choice according to strength and health. No more than *Nature* desires the mating of weaker with stronger individuals, even less does she desire the blending of a *higher* with a *lower* race, since, if she did, her whole work of higher breeding, over perhaps hundreds of thousands of years, might be ruined with one blow.

Historical experience offers countless proofs of this. It shows with terrifying clarity that in every mingling of Aryan blood with that of *lower peoples* the result was the end of the cultured people. North America, whose population consists in by far the largest part of Germanic elements who mixed but little with the *lower colored peoples*, shows a different humanity and culture from Central and South America, where the predominantly Latin immigrants often mixed with the *aborigines* on a large scale. By this one example, we can clearly and distinctly recognize the effect of racial mixture. The Germanic inhabitant of the American continent, who has remained *racially pure and unmixed*, rose to be master of the continent; he will remain the master as long as he does not fall a victim to defilement of the blood. The result of all racial crossing is therefore in brief always the following: To bring about such a *development* is, then, nothing else but to sin against the will of the eternal creator. And as a sin this act is rewarded. When man attempts to rebel against the *iron logic of Nature*, he comes into struggle with the principles to which he himself owes his existence as a man. And this attack must lead to his own doom. Here, of course, we encounter the objection of the modern pacifist, as truly Jewish in its effrontery as it is stupid! 'Man's role is to overcome Nature!'"

[Comment by PGH: "The will of the eternal creator," to use Hitler's language, is for all to care for the weak and least among us, but Hitler was trying to attribute to God the development (evolution) and preservation of an "Aryan" race. He did not know what he was talking about and was spiritually blind.]

Here the instinct of knowledge unconsciously obeys the deeper necessity of the *preservation of the species*, if necessary at the cost of the individual, and protests against the visions of the pacifist windbag who in reality is nothing but a cowardly, though camouflaged, egoist, *transgressing the laws of development*; for *development* requires willingness on the part of the individual to sacrifice himself for the community, and not the sickly imaginings of cowardly know-it-alls and *critics of Nature*. Especially, therefore, at times when the ideal attitude threatens to disappear, we can at once recognize a diminution of that force which forms the community and thus creates the premises of culture. As soon as egoism becomes the ruler of a people, the bands of order are loosened and in the chase after their own happiness men fall from heaven into a real hell.

[Comment by PGH: "critics of Nature" would be people like the present author who challenges evolutionary thinking. For Hitler, the law of Nature is essentially evolution.]

But the *natural law of all development* demands, not the coupling of two formations which are simply not alike, but the victory of the stronger and the cultivation of the victor's force and strength made possible alone by the resultant struggle.

[PGH: for Hitler, "the natural law of all development" is evolution.]

This will make them a precious national treasure to the entire nation; their growth must fill every single national comrade with pride and confidence, for in them lies the germ for a final, *great future development* of our own people, nay–of humanity.

If as the first task of the state in the service and for the welfare of its nationality we recognize the preservation, care, and *development of the best racial elements*, it is natural that this care must not only extend to the birth of every little national and racial comrade, but that it must educate the young offspring to become a valuable link in the chain of future reproduction.

For anyone who believes in a *higher development* of living creatures must admit that every expression of their life urge and life struggle must have had a beginning; that one subject must have started it, and that subsequently such a phenomenon repeated itself more and more frequently and spread more and more, until at last it virtually entered the subconscious of all members of a given species, thus manifesting itself as an instinct.

Thus, fundamentally, they serve the continuous process of *higher human development*. But the very same thing which once, in the form of the simplest ruse, facilitated the struggle for existence [Darwin's subtitle?] of the man hunting in the primeval forest, again contributes, in the shape of *the most brilliant scientific knowledge of the present era*, to alleviate mankind's struggle for existence and to forge its weapons for the struggles of the future.

No, the *natural development*, though after a struggle enduring centuries, finally brought the best man to the place where he belonged. This will always be so and will eternally remain so, as it always has been so.

ENDNOTES

Acknowledgements

[1] The background picture was taken by the river near Trick Falls at the Two Medicine campground (Glacier National Park, Montana), where the exposure of the Lewis Overthrust can be observed. The creek bed is Cretaceous and the upper layers are Precambrian. Presumably the Precambrian would have had to move fifty miles to get on top of the Cretaceous. Doug Sharp wrote, "We explored this area with Mike Oard to try to find the contact line." It is used here as a background because the dinosaur fossils pictured were found in Montana, though further to the east (at Hell Creek). The fossils themselves are on display at the Museum of the Rockies in Bozeman, Montana.

[2] Graphics art teacher and colleague Chris Fox graciously videotaped the entire assembly in May of 2001. It was well-received by the students. Copies are available for purchase through Skilton House Ministries. See chapter eighteen.

Introduction

[3] Cf. http://www.philly.com/mld/inquirer/news/special_packages/sunday_review/11763777.htm or contact Skilton House Ministries.

[4] For more on this, see chapter seven of this book. At least one reader called in response to the article, indicating that he would like to help with this particular ministry and worked to that end.

[5] "If a bird's nest chance to be before thee in the way in any tree, or on the ground, whether they be young ones, or eggs, and the dam sitting

upon the young, or upon the eggs, thou shalt not take the dam with the young: But thou shalt in any wise let the dam go, and take the young to thee; that it may be well with thee, and that thou mayest prolong thy days" (Deut. 22:6-7). The Lord, who instills in animals concern for their young, wants His people to respect that relationship. There is a related command: "When a bullock, or a sheep, or a goat, is brought forth, then it shall be seven days under the dam; ... And whether it be cow or ewe, ye shall not kill it and her young both in one day" (Lev. 22:27-28). Why this concern for animals and their young? The Lord Jesus, Maker of all (Col. 1:16; Heb. 1:10), said that His Father knows when a sparrow falls to the ground (Matt. 10:29). Some Christians, professing to believe the Bible, kowtow to academics who speak of animals becoming extinct supposedly millions of years before Adam sinned, the inference being that God must be cruel. The world became corrupt, however, through Adam and Eve; extinctions followed. The faith statement that the world is millions or billions of years old clashes with the words of Jesus. No academic went to a cross for sinners; Creator Christ did!

[6] Go to the ICR website and get poster: : AGU Poster by Dr. John R. Baumgardner – The Enigma of the Ubiquity of 14C in Organic Samples Older than 100 ka. See http://www.icr.org/research/ AGUC-14_Poster_Baumgardner.pdf.

[7] I can supply the reader with many references supporting this from journals like *Radiocarbon* and *Nuclear Instruments and Methods in Physics Research B*.

[8] See pp. 3-4 of the October 19, 1992 issue.

[9] This was the paragraph sent to the "PhD, DSc, Distinguished Professor of Human Genetics and Psychiatry."

Chapter 1

[10] "A scientist's view" by Richard Dawkins, *Guardian*, Saturday March 9, 2002.

[11] See page 28 of the May/June 1997 issue (Volume 17, Number 3).

[12] Paul G. Humber, *The Ascent Of Racism*, IMPACT No. 164 (Institute for Creation Research, PO Box 2667, El Cajon, CA 92021, Copyright © 1987). Many websites have picked up this article, as can be verified by typing the author's name (including middle initial) with quotation marks into Google.

[13] Sir Arthur Keith, *Evolution and Ethics* (New York: G.P. Putnam's Sons, 1947), p. 230.

[14] D. James Kennedy, "Ideas Have Consequences", Coral Ridge Ministries' *IMPACT*, August 2005, p.8.

[15] Ibid., p. 10.

[16] This notion has been challenged, but see the next chapter of this book.

[17] Adolf Hitler, *Mein Kampf* (Boston: Houghton Mifflin Co., 1943), pp. 286, 295, 325, 402, 403, 285, 289 respectively.

[18] Charles Darwin, *The Descent of Man* (London: John Murray, 1901), pp. 241-242.

[19] Ibid., pp. 291-292.

[20] Stephen Jay Gould, *Ontogeny and Phylogeny* (Cambridge, Mass: Harvard University Press, 1977), p. 127.

[21] Edwin G. Conklin, *The Direction of Human Evolution* (New York: Scribner's, 1921), p. 34.

[22] Ibid., p. 53.

[23] Henry Fairfield Osborn, "The Evolution of Human Races," *Natural History*, April 1980, p. 129, reprinted from January/February 1926 issue.

[24] Henry Fairfield Osborn, *Evolution and Religion in Education* (London: Charles Scribner's Sons, 1926), p. 48.

[25] Chris Mead, "Black Hero in a White Land," cf. *Sports Illustrated*, September 16, 1985, p. 94.

[26] Ibid., p. 92.

[27] "Gazetteer," *The Pennsylvania Gazette* (University of Pennsylvania), April 1986, p. 19.

[28] "Members Forum," *National Geographic*, March 1986.

Chapter 2

[29] Of course, this number is considerably higher now.

[30] See Helmut Krausnick and Martin Broszat's *Anatomy of the SS State*, published by Paladin, 1970, pp.29-30. See also, D. Gaeman, *The Scientific Origins of National Socialism: Social Darwinism* in Ernst Haeckel and the German Monist League xvi, 1971, where it says that Hitler "stressed and singled out the idea of biological evolution as the most forceful weapon against traditional religion and he repeatedly condemned Christianity for its opposition to the teachings of evolution .... For Hitler, evolution was the hallmark of modern science and culture, and he defended its veracity as tenaciously as Haeckel."

[31] Arthur Cochrane, *The Church's Confession under Hitler* (Philadelphia: The Westminster Press, 1962), pp. 40, 108, 268, 273, and 279. (See also Wilhelm Niemoller in *Kampf und Zeugnis der Bekennenden Kirche*, p. 526.)

[32] Roland H. Bainton (Marshall B. Davidson, Editor) *The Horizon History of Christianity* (New York: American Heritage Publishing Co., Inc, 1964), p. 390.

[33] December 17, 1981, p. D23.

[34] Nechama Tec, *When Light Pierced the Darkness: Christian Rescue of the Jews in Occupied Poland* (Oxford University Press, 1986).

Chapter 3

[35] They are Harry Akers, Kevin Anderson, David Bradbury, Robert Gentet, Ed Garrett, David Harris, Lane Lester, Ron Pass, Allen Roy, Dave Sack, Helen Setterfield, Curt Sewell, Doug Sharp, and Laurence Tisdall.

[36] Cf. http://palaeo-electronica.org/2002_1/editor/icon.htm.

[37] Cf. http://www.arn.org/arnproducts/books/b021om.htm.

[38] Cf. *National Geographic*, November 1985, pp. 574-7.

[39] Cf. *Creation Ex Nihilo Technical Journal,* 13(2):101-111, 1999.

[40] Cf. Chapter thirteen.

[41] Cf. Jack Cuozzo's book, *Buried Alive*.

[42] Cf. http://www.trueorigins.org.

[43] Cf. Derek Ager's *The New Catastrophism* (Cambridge University Press, 1993).

[44] Cf. http://www.creation.on.ca/cdp/articles/Lsu.html.

[45] Doug Sharp wrote that "it would be prudent to back that up with actual calculations. I used the figure of one chance out of 10 to the 123 power for the possibility of one protein being created by chance (avg. length 410 amino acids). This is from Coppedge: *Evolution Possible or Impossible.* The rest is calculated from the volume of the earth in terms of number of atoms and the distance in inches to the edge of the universe. I like this because it puts it in terms of extremes that people can fathom."

Chapter 4

[46] They, of course, are only walking or slow-trotting, but imagination is part of the game.

[47] The author was referring to the Lord's poetry in motion. Not wanting her to think that her husband was talking about himself, however, he added, "Not me," but then he remembered that he too was a part of the Lord's poetry. When the Bible says that "we are His workmanship," the Greek is *poiema* (poem—we are His poem). See Ephesians 2:10.

[48] It also points to a merciful Creator who cares for His birds (Matt. 10:29)—providing them with protective instincts.

[49] Charles Darwin, in the final paragraph of his *Origin of Species*, wrote, "Thus, from the war of nature, from famine and death, the most exalted object which we are capable of conceiving . . . directly follows."

[50] Creationists do not have a problem with natural selection. In fact, Darwin apparently "borrowed" this key concept from a creationist (cf. Chapter Thirteen), but natural selection has nothing to do with creating new genetic information and higher forms.

Chapter 5

[51] This was done and confirmed the earlier diagnosis; the AVM was still obliterated.

Chapter 6

[52] *Philadelphia Daily News*, October 28, 1986, p. 33.

[53] Kay Brigham, *Christopher Columbus - His life and discovery in the light of his prophecies* (Terrassa, Barcelona: CLIE Publishers, 1990), pp. 53, 61, 82, 85, 86, 115, 124, 125, 127, 129, 131, 167.

[54] Simon Wiesenthal, *Sails of Hope* (New York: Macmillan Publishing Co., Inc., 1973), p. 122.

[55] William Loren Katz, "'Ill Winds' Drove Columbus," *The New York Times*, October 8, 1979.

[56] Samuel Eliot Morison, "Christopher Columbus, Mariner," *American Heritage*, December 1955, p. 93.

[57] Samuel Eliot Morison, *Admiral of the Ocean Sea* (Boston: Little, Brown and Co., 1942), pp. 6, 206, 476, 494.

[58] Peter J. Marshall, Jr., and David B. Manuel, Jr. *The Light and the Glory* (Old Tappan, NJ: Fleming H. Revell Co., 1977), p. 41.

[59] Wilbur E. Garrett, "Columbus and the New World," *National Geographic*, November 1986, p. 564.

Chapter 7

[60] Skilton House Ministries, Inc. has been spearheading this effort, and the author has been serving as its Executive Director.

[61] See the Sunday, November 2, 2003 issue (pp. B1 and 5).

[62] *Time Well Spent* by Andree Seu, January 31, 2004, p. 43.

[63] For a copy of the report, contact School Ministries at 803-772-5224.

Chapter 8

[64] On June 10, 2003, the author inquired of Dr. Dawkins if he objected to the author's quoting him. He wrote back on the same day, "I do not object."

65 See http://www.aaas.org/spp/dser/evolution/perspectives/durant. shtml.
66 The audiotaped version of the report is either 115 or 150.

Chapter 9
67 E. Yaroslavsky, *Landmarks in the Life of Stalin* (Moscow: Foreign Languages Publishing house, 1940), pp. 8-12.
68 Conway Zirkle, *Evolution, Marxian Biology, and the Social Scene* (Philadelphia: University of Pennsylvania Press, 1959), pp. 85-87.
69 Ibid.
70 Stephen Jay Gould, *Ever Since Darwin* (New York: W. W. Norton and Co., Inc., 1977), p. 26.
71 Eduardo del Rio (pseudonym="Rius"), *Marx for Beginners* (New York: Pantheon Books, 1976), Glossary, n.p.
72 Harrison E. Salisbury, "Reading *The Gulag Archipelago* is like no other reading experience of our day," *Book-of-the-Month Club NEWS*, Midsummer, 1974, pp. 4-5.
73 Edward E. Ericson, Jr., "Solzhenitsyn-Voice from the Gulag," *Eternity*, October 1985, pp. 23, 24.
74 Aleksander I. Solzhenitsyn, *The Gulag Archipelago* (New York: Harper & Row, 1973), p. 7.
75 Henry Fairfield Osborn, *Evolution and Religion in Education* (London: Charles Scribner's Sons, 1926), p. 48.

Chapter 10
76 See *Beyond Fame or Fortune* by Lawrence Elliot, *Reader's Digest Book Section*, May 1965, pp. 259-310. Much of the material in this chapter was taken from this book condensation.
77 This was from the Internet, *Christian History Institute, January 5, 1943-Carver's Secret of Success*. See www.gospelcom.net/chi/DAILYF/2002/01/daily-01-05-2002.shtml.

Chapter 11
78 See chapter thirteen.
79 Harriet Beecher Stowe, *Uncle Tom's Cabin* (New York: Signet Classic/Penguin Putnam, 1998), p. 250.
80 "In 1987, nonwhite women were more than twice as likely to have an abortion as white women." See *The Philadelphia Inquirer*, July 5, 1992, p. E2. Statistics were provided by the Alan Guttmacher Institute.
81 The author's wife, Prudence, an RN, is one of them. She is Executive Director of Alpha Pregnancy Services in center city Philadelphia.

Chapter 12
[82] Paul G. Humber, *Evolution and the American Abortion Mentality*, IMPACT No. 227 (Institute for Creation Research, PO Box 2667, El Cajon, CA 92021, Copyright © 1992).
[83] Nathaniel C. Nash, "Mengele an Abortionist, Argentine Files Suggest," *The New York Times*, February 11, 1992, p. A8.
[84] Carl Sagan and Ann Druyan, "Is It Possible To Be Pro-Life And Pro-Choice?" *Parade Magazine*, April 22, 1990, pp. 5, 7.
[85] Elasah Drogin, *Margaret Sanger: Father of Modern Society* (New Hope, KY: CUL Publications, 1989).
[86] Margaret Sanger, *Woman and the New Race* (New York: Brentano's Publishers, 1920), pp. 44, 45, 63, 126, 159,226,229,232,234.
[87] Linda Gordon, *Woman's Body, Woman's Right* (New York: Grossman Pub., 1976), pp. 223, 332-333.
[88] Margaret Sanger, *The Pivot of Civilization* (New York: Brentano's Publishers, 1922), pp. 8, 25, 103, 113, 123, 170- 171, 263, 275-276.
[89] Raymond Pierpoint, Editor, *Report of the Fifth International Neo-Malthusian and Birth Control Conference* (London: William Heinemann [Medical Books] Ltd., 1922), pp. 31, 199.
[90] Margaret Sanger, "A Plan for Peace," *Birth Control Review*, April, 1932, pp. 107, 108. 10. Margaret Sanger, Editor, "Self Preservation," *The Woman Rebel*, April 1914, p. 16.
[91] Margaret Sanger, Editor, *Birth Control Review*, April 1914, p. 16.

Chapter 13
[92] Loren Eiseley, *Darwin and the Mysterious Mr. X* (New York: E.P. Dutton, 1979), p. 55.
[93] Ibid., p. 56.
[94] Ibid., p. 59.
[95] Ibid., p. x.
[96] Ibid., p. 108.
[97] *Seasonal and Other Changes in Birds*, pp. 112-140.
[98] Ibid., pp. 116-117.
[99] Ibid., p. 49. (Edward Blyth's sister wrote of him, "Never was any youth more industrious; up at three or four in the morning, reading, making notes, sketching bones, coloring maps, stuffing birds by the hundreds, collecting butterflies, and beetles—teaching himself German sufficiently to translate it readily, singing always merrily at intervals," p. 170).
[100] Ibid., pp. 68-69.
[101] Ibid., p. 54.
[102] Romans 1:18.

[103] Henry M. Morris, *The Long War Against God* (Grand Rapids: Baker Book House, 1989), p. 158.
[104] Matthew 10:26.
[105] I Corinthians 4:5.
[106] Hebrews 4:13.

Chapter 14
[107] It began in March of 1999, but as recently as November 14, 2005, he wrote, "I am very sad to hear the news of your mother's death. It is a very special thing to lose one's mother. In fact, many people never completely get over such a loss. My own mother died in 1975, my father in 1950. I've been an 'orphan' for so long that the times I shared with my parents seem almost unreal, like a story out of a book. You have been very fortunate to have had your mother so long. Please accept my deepest sympathy and condolence. Your friend, Frank."
[108] The other issue related to the question of the Lord Jesus Christ's existence. A paper was written by this author on this aspect, too. To get a copy, write to www.humber@juno.com.
[109] Date of correspondence, March 3, 1999.
[110] See John 8:13, 19, 25, 33, 48, 53, 57; 9:40; 10:24, 33, etc.
[111] Date of correspondence, February 3, 30, 1999.
[112] Carl Sagan and Ann Druyan, "Is It Possible to be Pro-Life and Pro-Choice?" *Parade Magazine*, April 22, 1990.
[113] Date of correspondence, February 31, 1999.
[114] Date of correspondence, July 5, 1999.
[115] Date of correspondence, May 21, 1999.
[116] Michael Parfit's article, "Before Noah, there were the Lake Missoula Floods" (*Smithsonian*, April 1995), shows prejudice even in the title. Nevertheless, the article admits to grand evidence for massive flooding in the American Northwest.
[117] Date of correspondence, May 26, 1999.
[118] See the *Program* of the Centennial Celebration of the Geological Society of America, 1988, A317.
[119] Guy Berthault, "Experiments on Stratification," *The Proceedings of the Third International Conference on Creationism* (Pittsburgh: Creation Science Fellowship, 1994).
[120] Date of correspondence, July 21, 1999.
[121] Mentioned in footnote 88.

Chapter 15
[122] Also written, Qur'an.
[123] Surat 7:54 is roughly equivalent to chapter seven, verse fifty-four. *THE HOLY QUR'AN English translation of the meanings and Commentary*, revised and edited by the Presidency of Islamic Researches (Medina, Saudi Arabia: King Fahd Holy Qur'an Printing Complex, no date), p. 413.
[124] Ibid., p. 2035-2082 (Index).
[125] Ibid., p. 140.
[126] Ibid., p. 28. See also S.7:166, p. 455.
[127] Surat 19:19, p. 857.
[128] See S.2:38 (p. 18), S.2:53 (p. 22), and quotations in the article.
[129] Surat 4:171, p. 272.
[130] Surat 5:17, p. 286.
[131] Surat 3:45 and 4:171.
[132] The title, Christ, is the Greek equivalent to the Hebrew title, Messiah.
[133] Isaiah 40:3,9-11.
[134] Surat 2:60, p. 24. Note, also, the plural "We" for deity.
[135] Exodus 17:6 (KJV).
[136] Genesis 16:7-13.

Chapter 16
[137] Institute for Creation Research in California.
[138] The colleague was an English teacher and would be familiar with this reference to Lewis' Narnia series.
[139] The author was quoting from a note the colleague had written to him; these were his words.
[140] Luke 16: 19-22
[141] 2 Corinthians 5:8
[142] Luke 23:43
[143] John 15:19
[144] Matthew 5:11

Chapter 18
[145] Matthew 2:1-3.
[146] The third letter is clearly the Greek letter, nu. The middle is less distinct, the left side seemingly missing. The middle (horizontal) line for the theta is present, however. The first letter looks more like an

omicron than an epsilon, but authorities have confirmed that this is a common variant. According to Guy T. Clark, "Judean coins from this period are nearly all crude and often have mistakes." He reported that he talked with David Hendin, adding, "All confirm that this is a known variant." This was a personal, handwritten note to the author, dated September 18, 1999.

Chapter 19
[147] See chapter one for a picture of the two of us during panel discussions. Persons who would like to purchase a videotaped copy may send $20 to Skilton House Ministries.
[148] From an August 6, 2005 e-mail message to me.
[149] It is not reproduced here because the author did not write a second time asking permission to use it again (for this book), but persons who would like to see it may contact me at humber@juno.com.
[150] *Dinosaurs,* by Peter Zallinger (Random House: New York, 1977).
[151] "A scientist's view" by Richard Dawkins. *Guardian,* Saturday March 9, 2002.
[152] "Moon, Mann, and Otto," by Stephen Jay Gould. *Natural History,* vol. 91, no. 3; March 1982, pp. 4-10.
[153] "Mysteries of the Deep—Natural laboratories in the oceans provide insights into the processes by which petroleum and metal deposits are formed" by Irene Kiefer. *Sci-Quest,* April 1982, p. 25.
[154] "Anything into Oil--Technological savvy could turn six hundred million tons of turkey guts and other waste into 4 billion barrels of light Texas crude each year" by Brad Lemley (photography by Tony Law). *Discover* Vol. 24 No. 5 (May 2003). See http://www.discover.com/recent_issue/index.html
[155] See www.changingworldtech.com/home.html.
[156] The reader is encouraged also to see D. R. Humphreys' book, *Starlight and Time: Solving the Puzzle of Distant Starlight in a Young Universe,* Master Books, 1994.
[157] Dr. Russell Humphreys, PhD in physics, has a book explaining this; cf. his *Starlight and Time.*
[158] More sophisticated C14 testing has been used also to confirm the Bible. See "Jerusalem tunnel built in 700 B.C.—Radiocarbon testing shows it is the same one mentioned in a Bible passage, researchers say" by Guy Gugliotto. *The Philadelphia Inquirer,* September 10, 2003, p. 10A.

[159] "Coelacanths—The Fish That Time Forgot," by Hans Fricke. *National Geographic*, June, 1988, p. 825ff.

Chapter 20
[160] Charles Darwin, *The Autobiography of Charles Darwin*, 1809-1882, Appendix and Notes by Granddaughter Nora Barlow (New York: Harcourt, Brace and Co., 1958, p. 58).
[161] Multiply 1/2 by 3/3 (a symbol for 1) and you get 3/6. Multiply 1/3 by 2/2 (another symbol for 1) and you get 2/6. 3/6 + 2/6 = 5/6.
[162] See Isaac Newton's *Principia* 1687, translated by Andrew Motte, 1729.

Chapter 21
[163] The debate took place on April 20, 2001 with approximately four hundred people in attendance.
[164] Photo supplied by Dr. Jack Cuozzo.
[165] Along the same line, the possible file marks on the La Chapelle tooth may suggest more sophistication in dentistry than is normally attributed to Neanderthals.
[166] He has since become executive director of the organization; there is a new president.
[167] Dr. Stringer eventually returned the disputed artifacts to the author by mail, who subsequently returned them to Dr. Cuozzo.
[168] There is evidence that other models with added teeth in the upper jaw have been made by this professor for distribution and possible sale.

Chapter 22
[169] Scribner's *Evolution and Religion in Education*, p.48.
[170] "No, sir, I couldn't … I wouldn't attempt to. I could possibly come as near as the scientists do, but I had rather be more accurate before I give a guess."

Chapter 23
[171] "How evolution became a religion: creationists correct?" *National Post*, May 13, 2000.

Appendix 1
[172] This way of thinking is very different from the culture, but the author is convinced that his life began at conception.

[173] The author's twin, Priscilla Hurlbut, lives in Sweetwater, TX, and has often served him in his writing.

[174] The McGaw School, now a museum.

[175] America's oldest public high school, 1634 AD.

[176] It was preached by Dr. Billy Graham.

[177] Students heading for college.

[178] The author also taught a humanities course.

[179] Spring Mill Baptist Church.

[180] Paul is married to Kristin; they are missionaries with Wycliffe Bible Translators. Ruth is married to Jeff Brittain; they live in Philadelphia.

To order additional copies of

EVOLUTION
EXPOSED

Have your credit card ready and call:

1-877-421-READ (7323)

or please visit our web site at
www.pleasantword.com

Also available at:
www.amazon.com
and
www.barnesandnoble.com